NEW TOUCHSTONES 14–16

Michael and Peter Benton

Hodder & Stoughton

A MEMBER OF THE HODDER HEADLINE GROUP

Orders: please contact Bookpoint Ltd, 39 Milton Park, Abingdon, Oxon OX14 4TD. Telephone: (44) 01235 400414, Fax: (44) 01235 400454. Lines are open from 9.00 - 6.00, Monday to Saturday, with a 24 hour message answering service. Email address: orders@bookpoint.co.uk

British Library Cataloguing in Publication Data
A catalogue record for this title is available from The British Library

ISBN 0 340 68346 5

First published 1998
Impression number   10 9 8 7 6 5 4 3 2 1
Year   2004 2003 2002 2001 2000 1999 1998

Cover photo from Tate Gallery Publications.

Typeset by Wearset/Peter Holroyd.
Printed in Great Britain for Hodder & Stoughton Educational, a division of Hodder Headline Plc, 338 Euston Road, London NW1 3BH by Redwood Books Ltd, Trowbridge, Wiltshire.

Contents

To the Teacher

THE *TOUCHSTONES* ANTHOLOGIES have undergone several revisions since their beginnings in the 1960s, the last of which was just prior to the advent of the National Curriculum in the late 1980s. *New Touchstones* brings the anthologies up-to-date with a thorough-going reappraisal of the series in the light of the National Curriculum requirements at the different Key Stages. Just as Matthew Arnold's original idea of a 'touchstone' needs reinterpretation in successive generations, so the principles upon which the series is based, while remaining constant, simultaneously reflect the changing cultural conditions in which poetry teaching operates. These principles have proved both popular and durable. They are:

(i)   that an anthology of poetry for pupils should have a generous inclusiveness which acknowledges that the poems pupils may enjoy, feel provoked by, remember and, maybe, find valuable are as likely to come from a jokey performance script by Michael Rosen as they are from a sonnet by Shakespeare. Pupils should be offered a wide variety of voices; their poetry experience should neither be restricted by narrowness of vision nor limited to specifically targeted purposes. We abrogate our responsibilities as literature teachers if we allow the boundaries of poetry in school to be set solely by that which is officially examined.

(ii)   that a mix of old and new poetry is important. It is as misguided to think that what is 'relevant' to 1990 pupils can only be poems written in the late twentieth century, as it is to promote the study of pre-twentieth century poetry merely on the grounds of its 'heritage' status. Poems by Donne or Blake can have a good deal more relevance to life today than contemporary poems that foreground the ephemeral preoccupations of the present. Yet, one of the advantages of poetry is its power to interpret the present for us. To set the work of recent writers in the context of that of their predecessors helps to illuminate the complementary qualities of both.

(iii)   that the concept of a 'teaching anthology' remains fundamental. The romantic notion that all teachers need to do is to read a lot of poetry to their classes so that its virtues, by some mysterious osmosis, will create a life-long love affair has long been discredited. Conversely, and far more apparent, there is the dislike that is generated in pupils by teachers who insist on line-by-line analysis which, in most cases, leads to the imposition of the teacher's views and the neglect of the pupils' responses. The approaches to teaching that we advocate are based on the premise that pupils' activities in reading and responding are the necessary preludes to their critical understanding of poetry.

(iv)   that 'creative' and 'critical' writing complement each other. Learning by doing is a natural process with poems. All pupils have something to say: by channelling their ideas and feelings into making their own poems as well as into commentary upon those of published poets, each informs the other. Pupils' criticisms gain the confidence of being written by 'practitioners' who have tried writing poems themselves; their imaginative writing gains from their developing knowledge of different forms and techniques.

New Touchstones has been composed with these principles in mind. It is constructed in three parts.

Part A: Ten Units

The purposes of this part of the book are to help pupils to enjoy and understand poems and to develop their knowledge of how they work. Each of the ten units aims to do three things:

(i)   to concentrate upon a main aspect of how poetry works, such as word sounds, imagery, or how feelings and ideas are expressed in different forms;

(ii) to give one or more examples of these aspects at work in particular poems; and,

(iii) to suggest ways in which pupils can talk and write about poetry and become more confident in expressing their views.

The units can be studied in any order. However, they have been arranged so that the first five deal with how we read words and images and gain a sense of the feeling that drives a poem; whereas the second five introduce the more technical matters of the rhymes, rhythms and forms which shape a poem on the page. None of these items can be separated out as neatly as this organisation into units suggests, but it is a convenient way of drawing attention to different aspects of how poems are written; it may also help to explain why some poems appeal to us more than others.

Where appropriate, we have included a brief list of poems elsewhere in the book which will take pupils further on the particular topic.

Part B: Ten Themes

Most poems are, by nature, 'solo performances' – responses to experience which stand on their own. Yet, similarities abound in subject matter, tone of voice, expressions of feelings and ideas, formal qualities and so on. While there will always be some sense of arbitrariness in thematic arrangements, nonetheless, it is clearly valuable to explore these similarities when they present themselves. The themes we have chosen are deliberately varied. Some are close to home ('Parents and Children' or 'Portrait Gallery'); others explore wider social and political issues ('War' or 'Work'). Some deal with intimate feelings and beliefs ('Is Love The Answer?' or 'Religious Experience'); others pose questions of life and death or take up an oblique or satirical stance towards human behaviour ('The Product I Tested Is LIFE' or 'Satires and Opinions'). The suggestions indicated by this icon for classroom activities at the end of each theme reflect both the autonomy of the individual poems and the advantages of comparative work. Talking, reading, writing, sketching, improvisation – all have a part to play in the study of poetry.

Part C: Ten Poets

The main criterion in this part of the book is to give a representative sample of each poet's work of sufficient substance for pupils to gain a clear sense of the writer's style, subject matter and way of looking at the world. The selection of poets was governed by the wish to include pre-twentieth century as well as contemporary writing and to indicate that poetry in English reflects a variety of cultural backgrounds. We did not want to duplicate material already published in our *Poetry Workshop* (1995) where, among others, James Berry and Grace Nichols were featured. Hence, in our twentieth century choices here, we opted for two English poets, one American, one Irish, one Welsh and one Scottish – lending, we hope, a distinctive regional flavour to this part of the anthology. Elsewhere in the book there are poems from cultures across the world, from China to the Caribbean, from Australia to Africa. We reject the distinction between 'our' and 'other' cultures, still evident in official curriculum documents, and the divisiveness it implies. The sheer variety of poetry in English is cause for celebration and sharing, not separateness. Poetry by John Agard or Maya Angelou *is a part of* an international literature in English *not apart from* it. The pages entitled 'Ten Poets: Workshop' (pp. 206–209) give some additional information about the poets we have featured here and suggest ways of exploring this material.

In the competition for time and attention in the National Curriculum, there is the danger that poetry is squeezed to the margins. When this neglect occurs pupils are short-changed; they are denied access both to that strand of literary history that has the longest and most distinguished pedigree and to an art form that has a peculiar ability to comment upon the culture and society in which they live. We hope that *New Touchstones* will encourage teachers and pupils to explore poetry widely, to enjoy the voices they encounter, and to gain a fuller knowledge of how poems work.

Michael and Peter Benton

PART A

TEN UNITS

'THE GOBLIN IN A WORD'

POEMS ARE MADE OF words; but, then, so are many things from text books to telephone directories. So what is special about words in poems? Ted Hughes compares the job of making a poem to capturing an animal and keeping its spirit alive. The key, he says, is to have control over the words, images and rhythms. Here is one of his 'captures' – a stag being pursued by the hunt. This verse comes half way through the poem where the stag has been hunted off its territory:

While everybody high-kneed it to the bank-top all along the road
Where steady men in oilskins were stationed at binoculars,
And the horsemen by the river galloped anxiously this way and that
And the cry of hounds came tumbling invisibly with their echoes
    down through the draggle of trees,
Swinging across the wall of dark woodland,
The stag dropped into a strange country.

In pairs

● Try reading this verse aloud. You'll need a deep breath. The lines are long and there are only three commas to help you reach the stag in line 6. Why do you think that Ted Hughes has written the poem in this way?

● Talk about the words, images and rhythms and how they combine to create this picture of the hunt.

● The complete poem is on p. 125. Hear it read aloud so that you can see this verse in context. List one or two words or phrases from each of the six verses that capture the stages of the story.

Ted Hughes continues:

'. . . as a poet, you have to make sure that all those parts over which you have control, the words and rhythms and images, are alive. That is where the difficulties begin. Yet the rules to begin with are very simple. Words which live are those which we hear, like 'click' or 'chuckle', or which we see, like 'freckled' or 'veined', or which we taste, like 'vinegar' or 'sugar', or touch, like 'prickle' or 'oily', or smell, like 'tar' or 'onion'. Words which belong directly to one of the five senses. Or words which act and seem to use their muscles, like 'flick' or 'balance'.

    But immediately things become more difficult. 'Click' not only gives you a sound, it gives you the notion of a sharp movement ... such as your tongue makes in saying 'click'. It also gives you the feel of something light and brittle—like a snapping twig. Heavy things do not click, nor do soft bendable ones. In the same way, tar not only smells strongly. It is sticky to touch, with a particular thick and choking stickiness. Also it moves, when it is soft, like a black snake, and has a beautiful black gloss. So it is with most words. They belong to several of the senses at once, as if each one had eyes, ears and tongue, or ears and fingers and a body to move with. It is this little goblin in a word which is its life and its poetry, and it is this goblin which the poet has to have under control.'

In pairs

● Add two or three words to each of Hughes's lists.

Hearing	Seeing	Tasting	Touching	Smelling
click	freckled	vinegar	prickle	tar
chuckle	veined	sugar	oily	onion

● Do any of the words you have added belong to more than one sense? Share your findings with the rest of the class.

Now, let's see how Hughes puts words to work in creating what he has called 'my first "animal" poem'. You will soon see why he puts inverted commas round the word 'animal'.

On your own

● Read the poem to yourself. Notice the situation. At the beginning the poet is sitting at his table, thinking about writing, gazing into the blackness of the night through the window. This blackness seems itself to be an image of his own mental blankness until the fox enters his mind's eye.
● Now, hear the poem read aloud.

THE THOUGHT-FOX

I imagine this midnight moment's forest:
Something else is alive
Besides the clock's loneliness
And this blank page where my fingers move.

Through the window I see no star:
Something more near
Though deeper within darkness
Is entering the loneliness:

Cold, delicately as the dark snow,
A fox's nose touches twig, leaf;
Two eyes serve a movement, that now
And again now, and now, and now

Sets neat prints into the snow
Between trees, and warily a lame
Shadow lags by stump and in hollow
Of a body that is bold to come

Across clearings, an eye,
A widening deepening greenness,
Brilliantly, concentratedly,
Coming about its own business

Till, with a sudden sharp hot stink of fox
It enters the dark hole of the head.
The window is starless still; the clock ticks,
The page is printed.

TED HUGHES

A poem about making a poem. How do the words, images and rhythms work together here?

In pairs

- Why is the poem given this title and not simply 'The Fox'?
- What do you 'see' when you read and hear the poem? Jot down your impressions of both the actual world of the poet's study and the imagined world of the fox emerging from the forest. Which seems the more vivid and real?
- List the words of the poem that belong to the five senses. Which sense is used most? Are all the senses appealed to in the poem?
- What do you notice about the shape of the poem? Note down anything that interests you about the rhyming sounds and the movement of the 'thought-fox' through these four-line verses.

Share your ideas with the rest of the class.

Ted Hughes commented about 'The Thought-Fox':

'This poem does not have anything you could easily call a meaning. It is about a fox, obviously enough, but a fox that is both a fox and not a fox. What sort of fox is it that can step right into my head where presumably it still sits . . . smiling to itself when the dogs bark. It is both a fox and a spirit. It is a real fox; as I read the poem I see it move, I see it setting its prints, I see its shadow going over the irregular surface of the snow. The words show me all this, bringing it nearer and nearer. It is very real to me. The words have made a body for it and given it somewhere to walk.'

(From *Capturing Animals* by Ted Hughes)

On your own

- Make your own 'thought-animal'. Use the blank space of a window, a wall or a sheet of paper to project your own mental picture. When the picture forms, write down the words and sense impressions to capture it as clearly as possible. Work up these notes into a short poem or prose description.

FURTHER POEMS

Ted Hughes:	'The Stag'	p. 125
Sylvia Plath:	'Morning Song'	p. 94
Dylan Thomas:	'Poem in October'	p. 102
Seamus Heaney:	'Trout'	p. 129
Seamus Heaney:	'Death of a Naturalist'	p. 186
Seigfried Sassoon:	'The Rear-Guard'	p. 66

READING WITH EYE AND EAR

With the eye. Look at any poem on any page of this book. The layout invites us to read it with an eye on the length of the lines, the gaps between sections or verses, and the spaces around the text. We read poems differently from the way we read stories. We *see* most poems as a *design* on the page.

With the ear. Read aloud any poem that appeals to you. Poems invite us to speak them with an ear to the rhythm of the lines, the pace of delivery, the sounds of the words. We listen to poems differently from the way we listen to stories. Try to *hear* the *music* of the verse as you speak the words.

In pairs

● How is the feeling of Spring created in the following lines? Read them through to yourself and then take it in turns to speak the lines aloud. At first, they may seem like a tongue-twister! Take care, the rhythms, sounds and stresses are tricky.

from: SPRING

Nothing is so beautiful as spring—
   When weeds, in wheels, shoot long and lovely and lush;
   Thrush's eggs look little low heavens, and thrush
Through the echoing timber does so rinse and wring
The ear, it strikes like lightnings to hear him sing;
   The glassy peartree leaves and blooms, they brush
   The descending blue; that blue is all in a rush
With richness; the racing lambs too have fair their fling.

GERARD MANLEY HOPKINS

● Talk with your partner about what you *saw* and *heard* when you read these lines.
● Now, read through the following poem to yourself and then hear it read aloud.

HERON

A gawky stilt-
ed fossicker★ a-
mong reeds, the
gun-grey-green
one, gauntly
watchful cold-
eye, stiff on
single column a
brooding hump
of wind-ruffled
feather-brain
feathering the
blue shall-
ows with one
scaly claw
poised drip-
ping—

★ delver

wades
the pebbled lake,
prints the mudflat,
scorns the noi-
sy fancy oy-
stercatchers' talk,
stalks, tall, to
his flat ramshack-
le nest or shack
of slack sticks
with three dull
greeny eggs
by a bul-
rush grove—

till the snaky neck
coils back
and strikes, beak
darts and spears
quick fish,
fish, fish
silvery-rich
fisher-king dish—

and then in the lone-
ly white lazy
hazy afternoon
he rises slowly
in a big zig-
zag heavy over
sultry fens
and windmill vanes,
flapping silently
in the land of wings.

EDWIN MORGAN

- Why is the poem laid out in this shape on the page?
- When you heard it aloud, what did you notice about the sounds of the words?

In pairs

The poem's four sections describe, in turn, how the heron stands on one leg completely still, wades towards its nest, spears a fish, and takes off over the water.

- For *each* section, write down the word or phrase *from the poem*,
  (i) which best describes the picture of the heron—four small verbal snapshots; and,
  (ii) where the sound of the words as you say them helps to create the sense of the heron's appearance or movements.

  Share your selections with the rest of the class.

FURTHER POEMS

METAPHORS AND SIMILES

HERE IN TEN LINES are ten creatures, finishing with another heron. The movements of each one are described by means of a comparison. Hear the lines read aloud.

from: MOVEMENTS

Lark drives invisible pitons★ in the air
And hauls itself up the face of space.
Mouse stops being comma and clockworks on the floor.
Cats spill from walls. Swans undulate through clouds.
Eel drills through darkness its malignant face.

Fox, smouldering through the heather bushes, bursts
A bomb of grouse. A speck of air grows thick
And is a hornet. When a gannet dives
It's a white anchor falling. And when it lands
Umbrella heron becomes walking-stick.

NORMAN MacCAIG

★ peg or spike driven into rock to support climber or rope

On your own

● Read through the verses again and then make three columns; the last one should be the broadest. Arrange them like this. We've started you off. Now complete the lists for all ten creatures.

1 *This creature…*	2 *…is compared with…*	3 *because its movement is…*
Lark	rock climber	noisy effort and stage by stage vertical ascent
Mouse	comma/clockwork toy	sudden shift from still shape; mechanical

These sorts of comparisons are called *metaphors*; they describe one thing in terms of another. It's fairly straightforward to list what is compared with what in columns 1 and 2; but you may have found column 3 more complicated.

As a class

● Talk about the ten metaphors and agree the first two lists.
● Now, work through column 3 and decide about each metaphor:
  (i) what is the precise movement described?
  (ii) are there any other characteristics of the creature suggested?

You should discover that one of the advantages of metaphors is that they carry several ideas at once; not only movements but colour, sounds, shapes and so on.

In the next poem the writer describes men admiring a girl in an open air tea-garden in Egypt. He has some fun at their expense by picturing them as different kinds of fish.

Hear the poem read aloud.

BEHAVIOUR OF FISH
IN AN EGYPTIAN TEA-GARDEN

As a white stone draws down the fish
she on the seafloor of the afternoon
draws down men's glances and their cruel wish
for love. Her red lip on the spoon

slips in a morsel of ice-cream. Her hands
white as a shell, are submarine
fronds sinking with spread fingers, lean
along the table, carmined at the ends.

A cotton magnate, an important fish
with great eyepouches and golden mouth
through the frail reefs of furniture swims out
and idling, suspended, stays to watch.

A crustacean old man, clamped to his chair
sits near her and might coldly see
her charms through fissures where the eyes should be;
or else his teeth are parted in a stare.

Captain on leave, a lean dark mackerel
lies in the offing, turns himself and looks
through currents of sound. The flat-eyed flatfish
sucks on a straw, staring from its repose, laxly.

And gallants in shoals swim up and lag
circling and passing near the white attraction;
sometimes pausing, opening a conversation:
fish pause so to nibble or tug.

But now the ice-cream is finished, is
paid for. The fish swim off on business
and she sits alone at the table, a white stone
useless except to a collector, a rich man.

KEITH DOUGLAS

As a class

- Identify the five metaphors used in the poem 'Behaviour of Fish in an Egyptian Tea-Garden' to describe the five types of 'fishy voyeur' in verses 3–6.

Now, re-read verses 1 and 2.

- In verse 1, what is the comparison used to suggest the girl's attraction for the men?
- In verse 2 her hands are described through two comparisons. What are they and what is the difference between them?

You can see that the comparison in verse 1, which reappears in verse 7, is a direct one introduced by the word 'as'; so too is the first one describing her hands in verse 2. These explicit comparisons using 'like' or 'as' are called *similes*; they tend to be less elaborate than metaphors and to focus on a single point of likeness.

Group readings

Three groups rehearse a performance. You will need someone to mime the girl (eating ice-cream, tending her nails and so on), a narrator to read verses 1 and 2 and the last verse, an 'important fish' (verse 3), a 'crustacean' (verse 4), a 'mackerel' (verse 5), a 'flatfish' (verse 5), and two or three others to suggest a shoal (verse 6) – perhaps nine in all. Divide up the lines and think about how you will present your reading.

FURTHER POEMS

Peter Porter:	'A Consumer's Report'	p. 42
Sir Walter Raleigh:	'What is our Life?'	p. 43
Dylan Thomas:	'Poem in October'	p. 102
Charles Causley:	'Ten Types of Hospital Visitor'	p. 109
Norman MacCaig:	'Frogs'	p. 122
Sylvia Plath:	'Morning Song'	p. 94

IDEAS INTO IMAGES

A DIFFERENT USE OF imagery can be seen in this poem by George Herbert, a seventeenth-century writer who was also a parish priest. Read it through to yourself a couple of times before hearing it read aloud.

THE CHURCH-FLOORE

Mark you the floore? that square and speckled stone,
    Which looks so firm and strong,
        Is *Patience*:

And th'other black and grave, wherewith each one
    Is checker'd all along,
        Humilitie:

The gentle rising, which on either hand
    Leads to the Quire above,
        Is *Confidence*:

But the sweet cement, which in one sure band
    Ties the whole frame, is *Love*
        And *Charitie*.

Hither sometimes Sinne steals, and stains
The marble's neat and curious veins:
But all is cleansed when the marble weeps.
    Sometimes Death, puffing at the doore,
    Blows all the dust about the floore:
But while he thinks to spoil the room, he sweeps.
    Blest be the *Architect*, whose art
    Could build so strong in a weak heart.

GEORGE HERBERT (1593–1633)

You do not have to be a church-goer to understand it. The poem falls into three parts: first, he identifies the stones of the church floor with different Christian virtues; then he tells us two short anecdotes; and the poem ends with two lines in praise of God. The whole poem is rather like a parable. Notice, too, how Sinne and Death, for example, appear in the poem as *personifications*, that is, they are spoken about as if they are real people.

In pairs

- Talk about how the different virtues are represented in the first four sections.
- What images do you get in your mind's eye of Sinne and Death?
- What is the idea in the image of God as the Architect?

Abstract ideas can sometimes be best expressed through images. Here are three poems about something we all experience all the time – days! Hear the poems read aloud in turn.

DAYS

Days, like sand, run through the hour-glass,
Flash by on the ticker-tape,
Turn the summer into winter,
Change the shape
Of facts and faces, rub out names
Cut with passion into tree-trunks,
Type out other ones instead,
Moss-fingered, fill the letters written
In stone to tell us who is dead,
Unweave the plover's nest in passing—
Days are egg-shells where I tread.

PHOEBE HESKETH

DAYS

What are days for?
Days are where we live.
They come, they wake us
Time and time over.
They are to be happy in:
Where can we live but days?
Ah, solving that question
Brings the priest and the doctor
In their long coats
Running over the fields.

PHILIP LARKIN

DAYS

They come to us
Empty but not clean—
Like unrinsed bottles

Sides clouded
With a film
Of yesterday.

We can't keep them.
Our task is to fill up
And return.

There are no wages.
The reward is said to be
The work itself.

And if we question this,
Get angry, scream
At their round clock faces

Or try to break the glass,
We only hurt ourselves.
The days remain intact.

They wake us up
With light and leave us
In the dark.

For night is not
Their weakness—but a tease
To make us dream of death.

There is no end to days.
Only a cloth laid
Over a birdcage.

VICKI FEAVER

In groups

Re-read the poems to yourselves. Notice that they all use images but in different ways.

- Phoebe Hesketh's poem is a list. How many comparisons does she use? Work through the items in her list. Which do you think are the most effective ones in suggesting the idea of days?
- Vicki Feaver's poem develops through three main images. What are they? What different qualities of days do they describe?
- Philip Larkin's poem asks two questions. It answers the first simply and directly; but the second is a puzzle. What does the image of the last four lines suggest as an answer?

On your own

- Think about the common threads that run through these poems: days as units of living, measures of time, hints at death ..... Write an essay comparing the three poems, saying which you prefer and why.

Here are three suggestions for a piece of creative writing:

- How do you imagine days? Make a list of comparisons and ideas as Phoebe Hesketh has done. Notice her days are active – they 'run through', 'flash by', 'turn', 'change' and so on. Write your own poem entitled 'Days' made up as a list of images.
- Alternatively, take a different abstract idea – God, heaven, hell, time, death – and jot down several images which, for you, suggest it. Then, work up your notes into a poem.
- What do you make of Magritte's *The Healer* (p. 13)? It is an image, this time not in words but in paint; but it also suggests ideas. Jot down how you 'read' the details of the picture. Work up your notes into a poem entitled **'The Healer'**.

The next two poems give us another angle on time and where it leads us. Hear the poems read aloud.

THE LEAVE TRAIN

The train is moving;
Out of the window I'm waving;
Sister, daughter, friend, and son
Wait on the platform unaware
The train has gone.

Behind them, relations, people
At parties, in shops, in the street—
People I know by sight but not to meet:
They cannot see
The light gone green for me
On a line untravelled.
One day they, one at a time,
Will take the train,
Each to a different destination
Not yet printed in the guide.
Yet every ticket's ordered in advance.

Under the clock they hurry
Home and back again
Making a dance of the time-table, believing
The train they must catch
Is not yet running.

PHOEBE HESKETH

NEXT, PLEASE

Always too eager for the future, we
Pick up bad habits of expectancy.
Something is always approaching; every day
Till then we say,

Watching from a bluff the tiny, clear,
Sparkling armada of promises draw near.
How slow they are! And how much time they waste,
Refusing to make haste!

Yet still they leave us holding wretched stalks
Of disappointment, for, though nothing balks
Each big approach, leaning with brasswork prinked,
Each rope distinct,

Flagged, and the figurehead with golden tits
Arching our way, it never anchors; it's
No sooner present than it turns to past.
Right to the last

We think each one will heave to and unload
All good into our lives, all we are owed
For waiting so devoutly and so long.
But we are wrong:

Only one ship is seeking us, a black-
Sailed unfamiliar, towing at her back
A huge and birdless silence. In her wake
No waters breed or break.

PHILIP LARKIN

On first reading, some poems can seem as obscure and indistinct as a photograph in a developing dish: you can make out some details but much of the image is unclear. Re-reading and note-making can help to give you a clearer picture.

On your own

Re-read the two poems.

- In Phoebe Hesketh's poem, 'The Leave Train', notice that lines 1–11 are about the narrator's train which has already gone. What is its destination?
- What does the second half of the poem say about the trains the rest of us will catch?
- Why is the poem called 'The Leave Train'? Write a single sentence to sum up what you think the poem is about.
- Philip Larkin's poem, 'Next, Please', sees events in time as ships sailing slowly towards us. What are the 'bad habits of expectancy' that we all have?
- Re-read the last verse. What picture do you get in your mind's eye? What is the idea that this image carries?

FURTHER POEMS

George Herbert:	'The Pilgrimage'	p. 79
William Blake:	'The Tyger'	p. 150
Christina Rossetti:	'Up-Hill'	p. 161
Stevie Smith:	'Not Waving But Drowning'	p. 51

FEELINGS INTO WORDS

WE HAVE ALL felt happy, unhappy, dislike, fear and a whole range of other emotions at one time or another; yet when we try to talk or write about our feelings the words often seem inadequate. Perhaps that is why we rely so much on songwriters (and poets) to express our feelings for us. Some poems go straight on to the attack, insisting on our attention, capturing us with images which seem to well up from inside and invite us to share the writer's feelings. Read the next two poems aloud. The first poem is a celebration by Grace Nichols of her young daughter, Lesley.

HEY THERE NOW!

(for Lesley)

Hey there now
my brownwater flower
     my sunchild branching
from my moutain river
     hey there now!
my young stream
    headlong
        rushing
I love to watch you
    when you're
      sleeping
        blushing.

GRACE NICHOLS

- What images does the writer use to describe her daughter?
- Why do you think she compares her to a young stream?
- What do you notice about the language she uses and the movement of the words?

Like Grace Nichols, Langston Hughes is a black poet, though he belonged to an older generation than Grace Nichols who is still writing.

DREAM VARIATION

To fling my arms wide
In some place in the sun,
To whirl and to dance
Till the white day is done.
Then rest cool at evening
Beneath a tall tree
While night comes on gently,
    Dark like me—
That is my dream!

To fling my arms wide
in the face of the sun,
Dance! whirl! whirl!
Till the quick day is done
Rest at pale evening . . .
A tall slim tree . . .
Night coming tenderly,
      Black like me.

LANGSTON HUGHES

● What feelings does Langston Hughes express?
● What pictures do the words create in your mind's eye as you read them?

Jeni Couzyn celebrates her delight at her baby asleep in her arms in a series of joyful images:

DAWN

Of your hand I could say this
a bird poised mid-air in flight
as delicate and smooth.

Of your mouth
a foxglove in its taking
without edges or hurt.

This of your ear
a tiny sea-horse, immortal
sporting in white waves

and of your eye
a place where no one could hide
nothing lurk.

Of your cupped flesh
smooth in my palm
an agate on the sea-shore

of your back and belly
that they command kisses.
And of your feet I would say

they are inquisitive and gay
as squirrels or birds
and so return to your hand

and begin my voyage
around your loveliness
again and yet again

as in my arms you lie sleeping.

JENI COUZYN

● Discuss the images that Jeni Couzyn uses and then hear the poem read again.

There are many poems in this collection where the writer finds ways of saying what many of us would like to say at times yet have never had the way with words to do justice to our feelings. W H Auden's poem 'Funeral Blues' on p. 91 is a good example. The penultimate verse reads:

> He was my North, my South, my East and West,
> My working week and my Sunday rest,
> My noon, my midnight, my talk, my song;
> I thought that love would last for ever: I was wrong.

The poem was little known by the general public until the success of the film *Four Weddings and a Funeral* where it was brilliantly spoken as a memorial poem at a funeral. The audience was stilled when it was spoken and the heightened sense of emotion that the poem created was always very powerful. Since the film it has become one of the nation's favourite poems.

● Look at the whole poem and ask yourself why these images should be so powerful.

We turn to poems and songs at times of deep emotion: poems to mark the passing of loved ones; poems to celebrate happy events – birthdays and marriages for example – and, of course, poems to express the love we feel for another. When we can't find the words ourselves we may buy a card that says something approximating to our feelings, or give our loved one a record of a song that says it for us.

In groups

● Discuss songs and poems that have touched you profoundly and share some of the images that you remember.
● Jointly make up a collage of lines and phrases from your collective memories for display.

RHYMES: COUPLETS: SOUNDS

Rhyme

When you were younger and you were asked to write a poem the first question was nearly always the same: 'Does it have to rhyme?' By now you will know that poems don't have to rhyme but there is a reason for younger children thinking that poems *ought* to rhyme.

The first poems we hear are usually nursery rhymes. Small children find them pleasing and satisfying partly because the rhyme makes them easy to remember. If you have contact with young children you will know they enjoy supplying the ending if you pause before the rhyme word:

> 'Jack Sprat could eat no . . . ?'
> 'Little Polly Flinders sat among the . . . ?'

In pairs

Read these two bits from well-known nursery rhymes:

> Humpty Dumpty sat on a wall
> Humpty Dumpty had a great fall . . .
>
> Mary, Mary quite contrary
> How does your garden grow?
> With silver bells and cockle shells
> And pretty maids all in a row.

● Where are the rhyme words in these two examples?

In 'Humpty Dumpty' you have simple rhymes at the end of each line called *end rhymes*.

In 'Mary, Mary' you have end rhymes (grow and row) but you also have rhyme words inside the line (Mary, contrary / bells, shells). These are called *internal rhymes*.

Here's another example you may remember:

> Doctor Foster went to Gloucester
> In a shower of rain;
> He stepped into a puddle, right up to his middle
> And never went there again.

There are three sorts of rhyme here:

● Which are the end rhymes?
● Which are the internal rhymes?
● One of the internal rhymes is not a *full* or *perfect* rhyme but what is known as a *half-rhyme*, that is a rhyme which although it sounds close, isn't a perfect match.
● Can you say which pair this is?

● Jot down any lines from nursery rhymes you remember from when you were much younger. Ring round the rhyme words from your examples and decide what kinds of rhyme they are: end rhymes, internal rhymes, full (or perfect) rhymes, half rhymes.

There once was a man from Nantucket
Who kept all his cash in a bucket;
    But his daughter named Nan
    Ran away with a man,
And as for the bucket, Nantucket.

You will almost certainly know some limericks, those five line poems that depend very much on a neat structure and clever rhyme for their effect. You can describe the *rhyme scheme* of a poem by putting the letter *'a'* by the first end rhyme and also by the next end rhyme which matches it; then *'b'* by the next end rhyme and by the next one which matches it – and so on. This limerick has, like all limericks, what we can call an *aabba* rhyme scheme:

A simple young fellow named Hyde	*a*
In a funeral procession was spied.	*a*
When asked, 'Who is dead?'	*b*
He tittered and said,	*b*
'I don't know, I just came for the ride.'	*a*

● Find, or remember, another limerick and write the rhyme scheme alongside it.
● What is the rhyme scheme of the two nursery rhymes quoted earlier, 'Mary, Mary' and of 'Dr Foster'? Remember, you only need identify the *end* rhymes.

The next poem uses rhyme in a quirky way by rhyming words when we do not quite expect it.

THE GREY SQUIRREL

Like a small grey
coffee-pot
sits the squirrel.
He is not

all he should be
kills by dozens
trees and eats
his red-brown cousins.

The keeper on the
other hand,
who shot him, is
a Christian and

loves his enemies.
Which shows
the squirrel was not
one of those.

HUMBERT WOLFE

● What is the rhyme scheme for this poem?
Rhymes help us remember lines. Advertisers know about and use the power of rhyme to give force to their message and make their products stay in our memories . . . 'A Mars a day helps you work, rest and play' or so, at least, they used to say.

In pairs

● Can you remember any examples of rhymed advertisements or 'advertising jingles'?

Rhymed Couplets and Epigrams

Rhyme, as we have seen from the limericks and the advertising slogans, can be used to give a sharp edge to a verse, add humour and make it more memorable. The first four lines of the limericks printed earlier in this unit are, of course, composed of two pairs of rhyming lines (*rhymed couplets*) though each couplet is of different length and instead of being complete in itself, looks forward to the fifth line which provides the punch.

Another nonsense form which uses just two rhymed couplets of irregular length is the *Clerihew* which was invented by Edward Clerihew Bentley:

Edward the Confessor
Slept under the dresser.
When that began to pall
He slept in the hall.

Clerihews are usually intended to be lightweight and absurd. A form of short, sharp, cleverly worded poem which makes a clever or serious point is called an *epigram*. Epigrams often use rhymed couplets to achieve maximum effect.

You might recognise some truth, in this two-liner from Ogden Nash:

Children aren't happy with nothing to ignore,
And that's what parents were created for.

Here is an epigram written by the eighteenth-century poet, Alexander Pope, to be engraved on the collar of one of the royal dogs at Kew palace. Imagine yourself bending down to see what was written there and reading:

I am his Highness' dog at Kew;
Pray tell me sir, whose dog are you?

Quite a put down: it's rather like being poked in the eye with a sharp stick!

On your own

● Using this poem as a model, try to write a two line epigram of your own. They could perhaps be lines intended to be found by somebody looking in your book or your private diary, or by somebody looking in your locker or bag without permission.

If you find it tricky, you might be spurred on by this ancient couplet describing a writer struggling for clever or witty thoughts and banging his head (pate) with his fist to see if he can force an idea out:

You beat your pate and fancy wit will come:
Knock as you please, there's nobody at home.

Alexander Pope was a master of the rhymed couplet and wrote long poems composed entirely of them. He was impatient with less skilful poets whose rhymes were obvious and predictable and complained about such writers:

Where'er you find 'the cooling western breeze,'
In the next line it 'whispers through the trees':
If crystal streams 'with pleasing murmurs creep,'
The reader's threatened, not in vain, with 'sleep'.

It is difficult avoiding the obvious rhyme in couplets – as all those old fashioned song writers found when 'moon' always rhymed with 'June' and 'love' with 'dove'.

● Can you think of songs yourself which annoy you by their too obvious rhymes?

Sounds

In one poem Pope attacks his enemy, Lord Hervey, who has been described as 'a minimy-piminy official' at the royal court, 'a man who was all airs and graces and intrigue, a sort of neuter', and who liked to spread unpleasant gossip and scandal. Part of it goes like this:

Yet let me flap this bug with gilded wings,
This painted child of dirt that stinks and stings
Whose buzz the witty and the fair annoys,
Yet wit ne'er tastes, and beauty ne'er enjoys . . .

Hearing it aloud, it is obvious that the rhymed couplets are important in giving a sharpness to the ideas. But there is something more. There is the *image* of the elegant Lord Hervey who would be dressed in fine clothes, silks, a powdered court wig and probably wearing make-up, being described as an insect to be swatted and there is the force of the *alliteration* in line two with the repeated *'d'*, *'t'* and *'s'* sounds that make the line so contemptuous in tone.

In pairs

● Try saying the four lines aloud so that you can feel the explosive force of the words and feel how you almost have to spit them out.
● Copy the first two lines of Pope's description of Lord Hervey and ring around each letter or sound that is repeated, drawing a line between each ring to show the complex pattern of sounds in the two lines.
● Compare your findings using the board and see if you agree.

Here are some examples of poets using words that seem to echo the sense in order to create a particular feeling.

● Try saying each quotation aloud and decide what the dominant sounds are and what effect they have. Are there long vowel sounds? short, staccato consonants? hissing sibilants? soft, caressing sounds or harsh, hard-edged sounds? quick or slow sounds? something else?

Often you will find that the writers are making use of what is called **alliteration**: the repetition of the same consonant sound in words or syllables:

Battle weary First World War soldiers in the trenches:
        Bent double, like old beggars under sacks,
        Knock-kneed, coughing like hags, we cursed through sludge . . .

                                      WILFRED OWEN

A shark: Pale ravener of horrible meat.

        HERMAN MELVILLE

An autumn day: Hedge Crickets sing; and now with treble soft
                  The red-breast whistles from the garden-croft;
                    And gathering swallows twitter in the skies.

        JOHN KEATS

A swallow: The swallow of summer, the seamstress of summer,
                 She scissors the blue into shapes and she sews it,
             She draws a long thread and she knots it at corners.

                                                    TED HUGHES

Rifle fire: Only the stuttering rifle's rapid rattle . . .

                                        WILFRED OWEN

Frogspawn: . . . the warm thick slobber
             Of frogspawn that grew like clotted water . . .

                                        SEAMUS HEANEY

A heron: . . . the snaky neck
             coils back
             and strikes, beak
             darts and spears
             quick fish, . . .

             EDWIN MORGAN

- Choose three of these quotations, write them down and ring round or underline similar sounds, joining them together with lines.
- Look through the rest of this book and find one quotation for yourself where you think the writer is trying to make the sound seem an echo to the sense.

FURTHER POEMS

Rhythm: Metre: Ballads

THE WORD 'RHYTHM' perhaps suggests an obvious regular beat, a pattern we can instantly recognise. Going back to our nursery rhyme examples in Unit 6 (p. 20) we find that most of them have a very marked rhythmic pattern of strong and light stresses. We can show the pattern by marking / for syllables with a strong stress and *x* for those with a light one or with no stress at all:

/ x   / x   /   x   / x
Mary, Mary quite contrary

Notice how the stress in 'contrary' is quite different and shifts to the first syllable if we say 'on the contrary'.

● Copy out the line below and mark the stresses using / and *x* for strong and light stresses.

Doctor Foster went to Gloucester

(Don't forget Gloucester is pronounced 'Gloster' and so has only two syllables not three.) There's a satisfying bouncy beat to the line that young children love. Similarly, in the limericks quoted earlier (p. 21) it is not just the use of rhyme that gives them lightness but also the bouncy and predictable pattern of stresses.

Where there is a regular pattern of strong and light stresses in poetry like this it is called **metre**.

Rhythm and metre are not the same. Rhythm can be much more subtle than it is in the examples we have seen so far. Almost everything we say – ordinary conversations, much of what we write – has an unobtrusive rhythmic pattern. Many of the poets in this book do not use an obvious, absolutely regular metrical pattern but rely on the rhythms of ordinary speech for their effects (sometimes to emphasise that they are talking to us). Rhythms such as these help hold poems together every bit as much as rhyme does.

Jennifer Armitage begins one poem quite conversationally:

And she is beautiful, our daughter.
Only six months but a person.
She turns to look at everything out walking.

There is a quiet, but perceptible stress three times in each line.

Robert Frost uses the easy rhythms of speech in his poem 'Mending Wall' which begins:

Something there is that doesn't love a wall
That sends the frozen-ground-swell under it;
And spills the upper boulders in the sun;

Can you feel how the even-paced movement of the verse suggests a quiet reflective tone? He is using one of the commonest and perhaps simplest metrical forms; the one known as **iambic** metre. Here the writer takes the simple light-heavy pattern (*x/*) and uses it as the basic rhythm of the line. If it is repeated five times in a line then it is known as an **iambic pentameter** (see p. 212). Usually you will find ten syllables in such lines:

$$x \quad / \quad x \quad / \quad x \quad / \quad x \quad / \quad x \quad /$$
And spills the upper boulders in the sun;

You will probably be familiar with the iambic pentameter from your reading of Shakespeare's plays which are largely written in this form. Rupert Brooke's poem 'The Soldier' (p. 69) uses iambic pentameter throughout:

$$x \quad / \quad x \quad / \quad x \quad / \quad x \quad / \quad x \quad /$$
If I should die think only this of me . . .

In fact, although this is the basic rhythm of the piece you will find some variations. It does not thump along quite so predictably from start to finish.

George Herbert, who wrote of the conflict he felt between being a priest and wanting to live a more normal life, captures the whirling passion of his feeling in the uneven rhythms of his verse when he tells of striking the altar or 'board':

I struck the board, and cry'd, No more.
     I will abroad.
What? Shall I ever sigh and pine?
My life and lines are free; free as the rode.

Hear it said aloud. The strong stresses dramatise Herbert's strong feelings. The rhythm and movement of the verse echo its meaning.

● Look through this book and see if you can find another example of a poem that uses the natural rhythms of speech. How does it affect the tone and movement of the poem?

Ballads

The ballad is a verse form that uses a fairly strict rhyme scheme and metre. It is very ancient and what it does is tell a story. Many of the traditional stories we know today only survived because they were originally ballads. They were not at first written down but dramatically told or even sung to a group of people: the Robin Hood stories were all originally very long ballad poems of this kind – one of them begins:

Lithe[1] and listen, Gentlemen,
That be of free-born blood:
I shall tell you of a good yeoman,
His name was Robin Hood

[1] Hearken

and it continues for over 450 verses.

The Douglas Tragedy (p. 27) is an early Scottish ballad which tells the story of the elopement of Lady Margaret and her lover Lord William and of what happens when they are pursued by Lady Margaret's enraged father and her brothers.

THE DOUGLAS TRAGEDY

'Rise up, rise up, Lord Douglas!' she says,
  'And put on your armour so bright;
Let it ne'er be said that a daughter of ours
  Was married to a lord under night.

'Rise up, rise up, my seven bold sons,
  And put on your armour so bright;
And take better care o' your youngest sister,
  For your eldest's away this night!'

Lady Margaret was on a milk-white steed,
  Lord William was on a gray,
A buglet-horn hung down by his side,
  And swiftly they rode away.

Lord William looked over his left shoulder
  To see what he could see,
And there he spied her seven bold brothers
  Come riding over the lea.

'Light down, light down, Lady Margaret,' he said,
  'And hold my steed in your hand,
Until that against your seven bold brothers,
  And your father, I make a stand.'

O, there she stood, and bitter she stood,
  And never shed one tear,
Until she saw her brothers fa',
  And her father who loved her so dear.

'O hold your hand, Lord William!' she said,
  'For your strokes are deep and sore;
Though lovers I can get many a one,
  A father I can never get more.'

O she's taken off her handkerchief,
  It was o' the holland so fine,
And aye she dressed her father's wounds;
  His blood ran down like wine.

'O choose, O choose, Lady Margaret,
  Will ye go with me, or bide?'
'I'll go, I'll go, Lord William,' she said.
  'Ye've left me no other guide.'

He lifted her up on her milk-white steed,
  And mounted his dapple-gray,
With his buglet-horn hung down by his side,
  And slowly they rode away.

O they rode on, and on they rode,
  And a' by the light o' the moon,
Until they came to a wan water,
  And there they lighted down.

They lighted down to take a drink
  O' the spring that ran so clear,
But down the stream ran his red heart's blood;
  And she began to fear.

'Hold up, hold up, Lord William,' she said,
  'I fear me you are slain!'
''Tis but the shadow o' my scarlet cloak
  That shines in the water so plain.'

O they rode on, and on they rode,
  And a' by the light o' the moon,
Until they saw his mother's ha',
  And there they lighted down.

'Get up, get up, lady mother,' he says,
  'Get up, and let in your son!
Open the door, lady mother,' he says,
  'For this night my fair lady I've won!

'Now make my bed, lady mother,' he says,
  'O make it wide and deep,
And lay Lady Margaret close at my back,
  And the sounder will I sleep!'

Lord William was dead long ere midnight,
  Lady Margaret long ere day,
And all true lovers that go together
  May they have more luck than they!

Lord William was buried in Mary's Kirk,
  Lady Margaret in Mary's Quire;
And out of her grave grew a bonny red rose,
  And out of the knight's a brier.

And the two met, and the two plait
  And fain they would be near;
And all the world might ken right well
  They were two lovers dear.

But bye and rode the Black Douglas,
  And wow but he was rough!
For he pulled up the bonny brier
  And flung it in St Mary's Lough.

ANON (one of several versions dating from medieval times)

In pairs

● Discuss what happens in the story.

● The tale is told very economically and concentrates our attention on a few key scenes. Verses 1 and 2 quickly tell us what has happened; verses 3, 4 and 5 tell of the flight and pursuit . . . and so on. Go through the poem and say what the other scenes are and what happens in each.

● Ballads often use clear, bright images often to do with colour: 'milk-white steed' is one. Can you find any similar images in the poem?

● What is the rhyme scheme for each verse?

● What is the metrical pattern for each verse? How many stresses are there in each line?

There are many variations in the ballad form but it is usually composed of four line verses often rhymed either *abab* or *abcb* with a 4,3,4,3 stress pattern though four stresses to a line are not uncommon.

● Try to write a ballad of your own. You will find it helps to focus you on a story if you choose and name a central character from the outset: somebody you know, somebody in the news, one of your heroes, somebody from history.

One class, instead of choosing a single character, decided to write a ballad about themselves 'The Ballad of 10JB' and celebrated the (often quite unbelievable) talents of the class in a ballad of 30 verses which they all worked on together with everybody contributing a few lines!

FURTHER POEMS

James Fenton:	'The Skip'	p. 50
Charles Causley:	'The Ballad of the Bread Man'	p. 82
B.S. Johnson:	'Song of the Wagondriver'	p. 114
Alfred, Lord Tennyson:	'The Charge of The Light Brigade'	p. 64
Peter Appleton:	'The Responsibility'	p. 73
Liz Lochhead:	'I Wouldn't Thank You For A Valentine'	p. 90
Benjamin Zephaniah:	'I Love Me Mudder'	p. 99
Maya Angelou:	'Phenomenal Woman'	p. 104
Thomas Hardy:	'When I Set Out for Lyonnesse'	p. 166

THE SONNET

THE SONNET IS one of the oldest verse forms in English. It is brief, flexible yet controlled by certain rules such that writers seem to enjoy breaking these rules or, at least, bending them to suit the demands of a particular poem. The list of 'further poems' (p. 34) shows all sorts of variations on the form, but basically the ground rules are straightforward: a sonnet must be composed of 14 lines, each one an iambic pentameter (see p. 212). These two rules govern all sonnets but the rhyming patterns vary according to which of the two styles of sonnet the poet is writing – the Italian or the English.

As a class

● Read out loud the opening lines of each of the four poems in this unit.

Immediately, you can see that the poems are about very different subjects: John Milton coming to terms with his blindness; Edwin Morgan describing a big city slum; Shakespeare poking fun at the exaggerated language of love poetry while at the same time praising his mistress for her beauty; Wilfred Owen creating a solemn anthem for his fellow soldiers dying on the battlefields of the First World War. Yet, they are all sonnets. The main difference between the two styles is brought about by their rhyme schemes. The Italian version usually changes after line 8 and lends itself to statement and counter-statement; the English version blurs this division and has a final couplet which often produces a witty conclusion or summary.

Now, let us look at the poems more closely.

The Italian Sonnet

John Milton, an intensely religious man, began to lose his sight in his late thirties and by the age of 44 he was totally blind. This poem, written in 1652, suggests his contradictory feelings at this loss, and his uncertainty about how he should continue to live a Christian life. Hear the poem read aloud.

ON HIS BLINDNESS

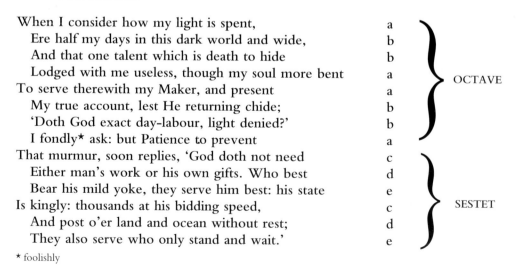

When I consider how my light is spent,	a
Ere half my days in this dark world and wide,	b
And that one talent which is death to hide	b
Lodged with me useless, though my soul more bent	a
To serve therewith my Maker, and present	a
My true account, lest He returning chide;	b
'Doth God exact day-labour, light denied?'	b
I fondly* ask: but Patience to prevent	a
That murmur, soon replies, 'God doth not need	c
Either man's work or his own gifts. Who best	d
Bear his mild yoke, they serve him best: his state	e
Is kingly: thousands at his bidding speed,	c
And post o'er land and ocean without rest;	d
They also serve who only stand and wait.'	e

OCTAVE (lines 1–8)
SESTET (lines 9–14)

* foolishly

- In the first 8 lines, how does Milton react to his blindness?
- The turning-point of the poem is the question in lines 7 and 8. What does Milton ask?
- In the last 6 lines, what is the answer he receives?

Notice that this sonnet in the Italian (or Petrarchan) style consists of eight lines, called the **octave**, rhymed on two sounds and arranged as two four-line units, *abba abba*. In the remaining six lines, called the **sestet**, three new rhymes appear arranged *cde cde*.

In pairs

Read through Edwin Morgan's poem about a rundown area of Glasgow. There is a deliberate irony in describing such a depressing scene in a sonnet – a form traditionally associated with love poetry.

GLASGOW SONNET

A mean wind wanders through the backcourt trash.
Hackles on puddles rise, old mattresses
puff briefly and subside. Play-fortresses
of brick and bric-a-brac spill out some ash.
Four storeys have no windows left to smash,
but in the fifth a chipped sill buttresses
mother and daughter the last mistresses
of that black block condemned to stand, not crash.
Around them the cracks deepen, the rats crawl.
The kettle whimpers on a crazy hob.
Roses of mould grow from ceiling to wall.
The man lies late since he has lost his job,
smokes on one elbow, letting his coughs fall
thinly into an air too poor to rob.

- Jot down some notes on the following:
  — The description moves like a film camera panning from detail to detail. There are two main shifts of focus after lines 4 and 8. What are they?
  — What picture do you get in your mind's eye of these three scenes?
  — What do you notice about the language of the poem and the rhyming sounds and patterns?
- Share your ideas with the rest of the class.

The English Sonnet

Shakespeare wrote the most famous sonnet sequence in the language; 154 poems in all, of which we can print just four (see also p. 146). His sonnet 'My Mistress' Eyes' was written partly as a reply to other writers of his day who produced fashionable but highly exaggerated sonnets in praise of the women (real or imaginary) with whom they were in love. Hear the poem read aloud.

SONNET 130

My mistress' eyes are nothing like the sun;	a
Coral is far more red than her lips' red;	b
If snow be white, why then her breasts are dun;	a
If hairs be wires, black wires grow on her head.	b
I have seen roses damask'd, red and white,	c
But no such roses see I in her cheeks;	d
And in some perfumes there is more delight	c
Than in the breath that from my mistress reeks,	d
I love to hear her speak, yet well I know	e
That music hath a far more pleasing sound;	f
I grant I never saw a goddess go—	e
My mistress when she walks treads on the ground.	f
And yet, by heaven, I think my love as rare	g
As any she belied by false compare.	g

Shakespeare teases these other poets and their ridiculous, overblown comparisons – 'My mistress' eyes are like the sun' was a fairly typical boast.

As a class

- List the fanciful comparisons Shakespeare mocks: eyes = sun; lips = . . . The first 12 lines deny his mistress all the conventional beauties – a risky business in a love poem!
- How does Shakespeare turn this to advantage in the last two lines?

As you see, the English (or Shakespearean) type of sonnet is constructed in three four-line units and a couplet. The rhyme scheme, therefore, is usually *abba, cdcd, efef, gg*. Sometimes there is a shift in the thought of the poem between the octave and the sestet (as commonly happens in the Italian sonnet) but often the poet will smooth over this division and, instead, use the final couplet as a unifying and summarising point of the poem.

Sonnets generally require a fair amount of working and re-working before the writer is satisfied with them. In order to show how one writer grappled with the writing of a poem that has since become one of the best known sonnets in the language, we have printed on the following pages the first and last of Wilfred Owen's four drafts of 'Anthem for Doomed Youth'. You may even notice that he sought out the help of another writer, Siegfried Sassoon, and that some of Sassoon's pencilled amendments are clearly visible.

In pairs

- What differences do you notice between the first and last drafts?
- Compare the opening four lines of the two versions and try to account for some of the changes. Does Owen make alterations simply to change the meaning, or to create certain sound effects or particular rhythms?
- Do you agree with Owen's final decision about the title? Why might he prefer 'doomed' to 'dead'?

Anthem for Dead Youth.

What passing bells for those who die so fast?
- Only the solemn/monstrous anger of our guns.
Let the majestic insults of their mouths
Be as the priest words/requiem of their burials.
Of choristers and holy music, none;
Nor any voice of mourning, save the wail
The long-drawn wail of high far-sailing shells.

What candles may we hold for these lost souls?
- Not in the hands of boys, but in their eyes
Shall many candle flames shine...
And Women's wide-spread arms shall be their wreaths,
And pallor of girls' cheeks shall be their palls.
Their flowers, the tenderness of ... minds,
And each slow Dusk, a drawing-down of blinds.

First Draft
(With Sassoon's amendments.)

Anthem for Doomed Youth by Wilfred Owen. This version shows Siegfried Sassoon's amendments marked on the manuscript. Note that at this stage, the intended title of the poem was 'Anthem for Dead Youth'.

Anthem for Doomed Youth

Nation

What passing-bells for those who die as cattle?
  – Only the monstrous anger of the guns.
  Only the stuttering rifles' rapid rattle
Can patter out their hasty orisons.
No mockeries for them; nor prayers nor bells,
  Nor any voice of mourning save the choirs,
The shrill demented choirs of wailing shells;
  And bugles calling for them from sad shires.

What candles may be held to speed them all?
  Not in the hands of boys, but in their eyes
Shall shine the holy glimmers of goodbyes.
  And The pallor of girls' brows shall be their pall;
Their flowers the tenderness of silent minds,
  And each slow dusk a drawing-down of blinds.

Anthem for Doomed Youth – final draft.

FURTHER POEMS

SYLLABIC FORMS

SYLLABIC VERSE, AS its name suggests, depends upon the lines having a set number of syllables. Thom Gunn's poem 'Considering the Snail' is syllabic verse. How many syllables are there to each line? (Occasionally you will have to count the syllables you *hear* as it is read rather than the actual number of syllables.)

CONSIDERING THE SNAIL

The snail pushes through a green
night, for the grass is heavy
with water and meets over
the bright path he makes, where rain
has darkened the earth's dark. He
moves in a wood of desire,

pale antlers barely stirring
as he hunts. I cannot tell
what power is at work, drenched there
with purpose, knowing nothing.
What is a snail's fury? All
I think is that if later

I parted the blades above
the tunnel and saw the thin
trail of broken white across
litter, I would never have
imagined the slow passion
to that deliberate progress

THOM GUNN

Syllabic verse is a fairly easy, light structure and often has a conversational tone. Some poets feel strongly that simply counting syllables can lead to bad verse where almost anything goes. The poet John Heath-Stubbs said that syllabic verse was 'a device whereby incompetent poetasters can set something down on the page which looks like verse but isn't'. That is probably true but it doesn't mean that if something is syllabic it is necessarily bad. For a syllabic poem not to sound plodding and dull, there has to be something more than syllables.

As a class

● Discuss Thom Gunn's poem above and decide what other things, apart from the fact that it has a certain number of syllables to each line, make it a poem rather than prose chopped up into equal lengths.
● What do you make of the lines below taken from a poem about pigeons by Fiona Pitt-Kethley?

I used to love to watch their delicate
shades of grey as they swaggered on the lawn
jostling for bits of bread I'd left for them

Some syllabic verse follows quite strict structures. One with which you may already be familiar is the *haiku*. This is a very short Japanese form of 17 syllables arranged in a particular pattern. In the English version of the form it is usual to arrange the syllables in three lines with five syllables in the first line, seven in the second and five in the third:

BAMBOO GROVE

Song of the cuckoo
In the grove of great bamboos,
Moonlight seeping through.

BASHO

Although the translator has chosen to rhyme the first and third lines this is not in fact strictly necessary. Notice how the writer tries to concentrate our imagination on recreating a single image in our imagination.

Over 25 years ago a school student, asked by her teacher to write a haiku, looked out of the classroom window and saw an approaching storm. Blue-black clouds massed behind a line of tall, green Lombardy poplar trees which bent almost double as the first violent wind hit them. She wrote:

Green as the stream flows,
Flickering whipcord in the wind,
Lombardy thrashes.

The image lives on.

On your own

● Try to write your own haiku poem where you focus on a single image and try to capture it in 17 syllables. You could choose a scene as Basho did (many haiku poems are about the natural world) or you could choose to focus on something immediately before you – your hand, the blank sheet of paper, the clock on the wall . . .

A *Cinquain*, which is a form developed in America, has five lines. They are arranged as a syllabic pattern with two syllables in the first line, four in the second, six in the third, eight in the fourth and then back to two syllables in the fifth and last line – 22 syllables in all. The cinquain below was written by a school student.

MR DEATH AT THE DOOR

Butler,
Open up for
It is Mr Death come
To see how well I am doing.
How kind!

REBECCA BAZELEY

Again, there is more to the poem than just having the right number of syllables.

● Discuss what images and ideas the poem conjures up in your mind.
● Now try your hand at writing a cinquain of your own. If you have problems getting

started, you might like to use Rebecca Bazeley's idea of focusing on a person in the first line. 'Butler' she begins: where might a cinquain beginning 'Teacher' or 'Mother', for example, lead your thoughts?

There are many other syllabic forms. The Japanese *tanka*, for instance, has syllables arranged in 5,7,5,7,7 pattern. All are worth experimenting with and it is interesting to see how they will not come alive on the page unless there is an idea, a spark to fire our imagination. Neatly arranged syllables alone are not enough!

At its best, syllabic verse makes real use of the structure that syllable counting requires of the poet. Sylvia Plath has a particular idea in mind when she has us syllable counting and indeed line counting and even letter counting in the title, in her remarkable poem 'Metaphors'. Each line is an image, a metaphor, a way of looking at the same thing.

As a class

● Listen to the poem being read aloud and ask yourself how it works, what the significance is of each of the metaphors and why counting is so important.

METAPHORS

I'm a riddle in nine syllables
An elephant, a ponderous house.
A melon strolling on two tendrils.
Oh, red fruit, ivory, fine timbers!
This loaf's big with its yeasty rising.
Money's new minted in this fat purse.
I'm a means, a stage, a cow in calf.
I've eaten a bag of green apples,
Boarded the train there's no getting off.

SYLVIA PLATH

FREE VERSE

FREE VERSE POETRY makes little or no use of traditional rhyme and metre or of the kinds of forms and structures we have mentioned in previous units and yet it still has the appearance and feel of verse. Look at the next poem.

FLIGHT OF THE ROLLER COASTER

Once more around should do it, the man confided . . .

And sure enough, when the roller-coaster reached the peak
Of the giant curve above me—screech of its wheels
Almost drowned by the shriller cries of the riders—

Instead of the dip and plunge with its landslide of screams
It rose in the air like a movieland magic carpet, some wonderful bird,

And without fuss or fanfare swooped slowly across the amusement park,
Over Spook's Castle, ice-cream booths, shooting-gallery; and losing no height

Made the last yards above the beach, where the cucumber-cool
Brakeman in the last seat saluted
A lady about to change from her bathing-suit.

Then, as many witnesses duly reported, headed leisurely over the water,
Disappearing mysteriously all too soon behind a low-lying flight of clouds.

RAYMOND SOUSTER

Modern poets often use free verse and you will find many examples in this collection. The words of a free verse poem are not organised into a symmetrical pattern with a regular metre and a rhyme scheme, yet it would be wrong to think of this kind of verse as being formless. Some of it certainly is but in good free verse the shape and structure of the poem reflect the mood and meaning of the writer; the organisation of the poem arises directly out of what the poet wants to say. D.H. Lawrence was probably one of the most skilful writers of free verse. You may well have come across some of his animal poems already – 'Bat', 'Mosquito', 'Mountain Lion' and 'Snake' are some of the best known. Here is the opening of another of his animal poems, 'Baby Tortoise'.

You know what it is to be born alone,
Baby tortoise!

The first day to heave your feet little by little from the shell,
Not yet awake,
And remain lapsed on earth,
Not quite alive.

A tiny, fragile, half-animate bean.
To open your tiny beak-mouth, that looks as if it would never open,
Like some iron door;
To lift the upper hawk-beak from the lower base
And reach your skinny little neck
And take your first bite at some dim bit of herbage,
Alone, small insect,
Tiny bright-eye,
Slow one,
To take your first solitary bite
And move on your slow, solitary hunt.
Your bright, dark little eye,
Your eye of a dark disturbed night,
Under its slow lid, tiny baby tortoise,
So indomitable.

- Which is the longest line, and which is the shortest?
- Which is the longest sentence and which is the shortest?
- Which words occur more than once at the beginning of lines?
- Why do you think the description is split up into two short sections and then a long one?
- Does the way the lines are arranged on the page make any difference to the way the poem reads? Would it be the same if it were printed as a solid block of prose?

Lawrence uses the rhythms of everyday speech and by giving the words a shape on the page he gives us directions as to how to hear the poem and how to speak it. The American poet, William Carlos Williams also used the simple rhythms of ordinary language but was much more a minimalist than Lawrence. Rather like the Japanese haiku poets, he focuses us so intensely on the ordinary that we see how extraordinary it can be. In this free verse poem we almost see through a painter's eyes:

THE RED WHEELBARROW

so much depends
upon

a red wheel
barrow

glazed with rain
water

beside the white
chickens.

WILLIAM CARLOS WILLIAMS

As a class

- Discuss whether it would make any difference to the way you see the words and the way you would say them if it were written like this on the page:

So much depends upon a red wheel barrow glazed with rain water beside the white chickens.

On your own

You may well have written some free verse poems of your own already, but now that you have had the opportunity to discuss this form more fully try it again.

- Choose your own subject. If you would like an idea to start you off, you could try continuing Raymond Souster's poem yourself: where did the roller coaster go after it disappeared behind the bank of cloud? Or try writing your own animal description with the same kind of intense attention to detail that D.H. Lawrence shows in his poem.
- Remember: don't worry about rhyme or regular metre. Try the lines over to yourself in your head and choose line lengths that suit what it is you are trying to say; leave out any words that are not earning their keep; try for a piece that isn't simply chopped up prose.
- Work over your first version with these ideas in mind until you feel it says what you want it to say in the most economical way possible. Don't be afraid to ask for advice.

FURTHER POEMS

TEN THEMES

'THE PRODUCT I TESTED IS LIFE'

A CONSUMER'S REPORT

The name of the product I tested is LIFE.
I have completed the form you sent me
and understand that my answers are confidential.

I had it as a gift,
I didn't feel much while using it,
in fact, I think I'd have liked to be more excited.
It seemed gentle on the hands
but left an embarrassing deposit behind.
It was not economical
and I have used much more than I thought
(I suppose I have about half left
but it's difficult to tell)—
Although the instructions are fairly large
there are so many of them
I don't know which to follow, especially
as they seem to contradict each other.
I'm not sure such a thing
should be put in the way of children
(heaven knows they're growing up
quickly enough already);
it's difficult to think of a purpose
for it. One of my friends says
it's just to keep its maker in a job.
Also the price is much too high.
Things are piling up so fast,
after all, the world got by
for a thousand million years
without this, do we need it now?
(Incidentally, please ask your man
to stop calling me 'the respondent';
I don't like the sound of it.)
There seem to be a lot of different labels,
sizes and colours should be uniform,
the shape is awkward, it's waterproof
but not heat-resistant, it doesn't keep
yet it's very difficult to get rid of.
Whenever they make it cheaper they seem
to put less in: if you say you don't
want it, then it's delivered anyway—
I'd agree it's a popular product,
it's got into the language; people

even say they're on the side of it.
Personally I think it's overdone,
a small thing people are ready
to behave badly about. I think
we should take it for granted. If its
experts are called philosophers or market
researchers or historians, we shouldn't
care. We are the consumers and the last
law makers. So finally, I'd buy it.
But the question of a 'best buy'
I'd like to leave until I get
the competitive product you said you'd send.

PETER PORTER

WHAT IS OUR LIFE?

What is our life? A play of passion.
And what our mirth but music of division?
Our mothers' wombs the tiring★ houses be
Where we are dressed for this short comedy.
Heaven the judicious sharp spectator is
Who sits and marks what here we do amiss.
The graves that hide us from the searching sun
Are like drawn curtains when the play is done.
Thus playing post we to our latest rest,
And then we die in earnest, not in jest.

SIR WALTER RALEIGH (?1554–1618)

★ dressing rooms for actors

UPON A DEAD MAN'S HEAD

Your ugly token
My mind hath broken
From worldly lust:
For I have discust
We are but dust,
And die we must.
  It is general
To be mortal:
I have well espied
No man may him hide
From Death hollow-eyed,
With sinews wyderèd[1],   [1] withered
With bones shyderèd,
With his worm-eaten maw,
And his ghastly jaw
Gasping aside,

Naked of hide,
Neither flesh nor fell.
　　Then, by my counsel,
Look that ye spell
Well this gospel:
For whereso we dwell
Death will us quell,
And with us mell.
　　For all our pampered paunches
There may no fraunchis[2],
Nor worldly bliss,
Redeem us from this:
Our days be dated
To be checkmated
With draughtes of death
Stopping our breath:
Our eyen sinking,
Our bodies stinking,
Our gummes grinning,
Our soules brinning[3].
To whom, then, shall we sue,
For to have rescue,
But to sweet Jesu
On us then for to rue[4]?
　　O goodly Child
Of Mary mild,
Then be our shield!
That we be not exiled
To the dyne[5] dale
Of bootless bale[6],
Nor to the lake
Of fiendes black.
　　But grant us grace
To see thy Face,
And to purchase
Thine heavenly place,
And thy palace
Full of solace
Above the sky
That is so high;
Eternally
To behold and see
The Trinity!
　　Amen.

JOHN SKELTON (?1460–1529)

[2] privilege　　[3] burning　　[4] be sorry　　[5] noisy　　[6] torment

TO DAFFODILS

Fair daffodils, we weep to see
  You haste away so soon;
As yet the early-rising sun
  Has not attained his noon.
      Stay, stay
    Until the hasting day
      Has run
    But to the evensong;
And, having prayed together, we
    Will go with you along.

We have short time to stay as you,
  We have as short a spring;
As quick a growth to meet decay,
  As you, or anything.
      We die
    As your hours do, and dry
      Away
    Like to the summer's rain;
Or as the pearls of morning's dew,
    Ne'er to be found again.

ROBERT HERRICK (1591–1674)

SIC VITA

  Like to the falling of a star,
Or as the flights of eagles are,
Or like the fresh spring's gaudy hue,
Or silver drops of morning dew,
Or like a wind that chafes the flood,
Or bubbles which on water stood:
Even such is man, whose borrowed light
Is straight called in, and paid to night.

    The wind blows out, the bubble dies;
    The spring entombed in autumn lies;
    The dew dries up, the star is shot;
    The flight is past: and man forgot.

HENRY KING (1592–1669)

NEITHER OUT FAR NOR IN DEEP

The people along the sand
All turn and look one way.
They turn their back on the land.
They look at the sea all day.

As long as it takes to pass
A ship keeps raising its hull;
The wetter ground like glass
Reflects a standing gull.

The land may vary more;
But wherever the truth may be—
The water comes ashore,
And the people look at the sea.

They cannot look out far.
They cannot look in deep.
But when was that ever a bar
To any watch they keep?

ROBERT FROST

SITTING SIDEWAYS TO THE SEA

While some look skyward from the sand,
And some horizon-watchers be,
And others sternly face the land,
We're sitting sideways to the sea.

While some build castles in the air,
And some the Ship of Death can see,
And some kick pebbles of despair,
We're sitting sideways to the sea.

While some see visions in the clouds,
And some, signs of Eternity,
And some anticipate their shrouds
We're sitting sideways to the sea.

This sideways-sitting pose, you see,
Directs our eyes along the beach;
We face the future knee to knee.
And never look beyond our reach.

MICHAEL BENTON

IF

If you can keep your head when all about you
   Are losing theirs and blaming it on you,
If you can trust yourself when all men doubt you,
   But make allowance for their doubting too;
If you can wait and not be tired by waiting,
   Or being lied about, don't deal in lies,
Or being hated don't give way to hating,
   And yet don't look too good, nor talk too wise:

If you can dream—and not make dreams your master;
   If you can think—and not make thoughts your aim,
If you can meet with Triumph and Disaster
   And treat these two impostors just the same;
If you can bear to hear the truth you've spoken
   Twisted by knaves to make a trap for fools,
Or watch the things you gave your life to, broken,
   And stoop and build 'em up with worn-out tools:

If you can make one heap of all your winnings
   And risk it on one turn of pitch-and-toss,
And lose, and start again at your beginnings
   And never breathe a word about your loss;
If you can force your heart and nerve and sinew
   To serve your turn long after they are gone,
And so hold on when there is nothing in you
   Except the Will which says to them: 'Hold on!'

If you can talk with crowds and keep your virtue,
   Or walk with Kings—nor lose the common touch,
If neither foes nor loving friends can hurt you,
   If all men count with you, but none too much;
If you can fill the unforgiving minute
   With sixty seconds' worth of distance run,
Yours is the Earth and everything that's in it,
   And—which is more—you'll be a Man, my son!

RUDYARD KIPLING

YOU WILL BE HEARING FROM US SHORTLY

You feel adequate to the demands of this position?
What qualities do you feel you
Personally have to offer?

                                        Ah

Let us consider your application form.
Your qualifications, though impressive are
Not, we must admit, precisely what
We had in mind. Would you care
To defend their relevance?

                                          Indeed

Now your age. Perhaps you feel able
To make your own comment about that,
Too? We are conscious ourselves
Of the need for a candidate with precisely
The right degree of immaturity.

                                          So glad we agree

And now a delicate matter: your looks.
You do appreciate this work involves
Contact with the actual public? Might they,
Perhaps, find your appearance
Disturbing?

                                          Quite so

And your accent. That is the way
You have always spoken, is it? What
Of your education? Were
You educated? We mean, of course,
Where were you educated?
And how
Much of a handicap is that to you.
Would you say?

                   Married, children,
We see. The usual dubious
Desire to perpetuate what had better
Not have happened at all. We do not
Ask what domestic disasters shimmer
Behind that vaguely unsuitable address.

And you were born—?

                                          Yes. Pity.

So glad we agree.

U.A. FANTHORPE

DEFYING GRAVITY

Gravity is one of the oldest tricks in the book.
Let go of the book and it abseils to the ground
As if, at the centre of the earth, spins a giant yo-yo
To which everything is attached by an invisible string.

Tear out a page of the book and make an aeroplane.
Launch it. For an instant it seems that you have fashioned
A shape that can outwit air, that has slipped the knot.
But no. The earth turns, the winch tightens, it is wound in.

One of my closest friends is, at the time of writing,
Attempting to defy gravity, and will surely succeed.
Eighteen months ago he was playing rugby,
Now, seven stones lighter, his wife carries him aw–

Kwardly from room to room. Arranges him gently
Upon the sofa for the visitors. 'How are things?'
Asks one, not wanting to know. Pause. 'Not too bad.'
(Open brackets. Condition inoperable. Close brackets.)

Soon now, the man that I love (not the armful of bones)
Will defy gravity. Freeing himself from the tackle
He will sidestep the opposition and streak down the wing
Towards a dimension as yet unimagined.

Back where the strings are attached there will be a service
And homage paid to the giant yo-yo. A box of left-overs
Will be lowered into a space on loan from the clay.
Then, weighted down, the living will walk wearily away.

ROGER McGOUGH

THE SKIP

I took my life and threw it on the skip,
Reckoning the next-door neighbours wouldn't mind
If my life hitched a lift to the council tip
With their dry rot and rubble. What you find

With skips is—the whole community joins in.
Old mattresses appear, doors kind of drift
Along with all that won't fit in the bin
And what the bin-men can't be fished to shift.

I threw away my life, and there it lay
And grew quite sodden. 'What a dreadful shame,'
Clucked some old bag and sucked her teeth: 'The way
The young these days . . . no values . . . me, I blame . . . '

But I blamed no one. Quality control
Had loused it up, and that was that. 'Nough said.
I couldn't stick at home. I took a stroll
And passed the skip, and left my life for dead.

Without my life, the beer was just as foul,
The landlord still as filthy as his wife,
The chicken in the basket was an owl,
And no one said: 'Ee, Jim-lad, whur's thee life?'

Well, I got back that night the worse for wear,
But still just capable of single vision;
Looked in the skip; my life—it wasn't there!
Some bugger'd nicked it—*without* my permission.

Okay, so I got angry and began
To shout, and woke the street. Okay. *Okay!*
And I was sick all down the neighbour's van.
And I disgraced myself on the par-*kay*.

And then . . . you know how if you've had a few
You'll wake at dawn, all healthy, like sea breezes,
Raring to go, and thinking: 'Clever you!
You've got away with it.' And then, oh Jesus,

It hits you. Well, that morning, just at six
I woke, got up and looked down at the skip.
There lay my life, still sodden, on the bricks;
There lay my poor old life, arse over tip.

Or was it mine? Still dressed, I went downstairs
And took a long cool look. The truth was dawning.
Someone had just exchanged my life for theirs.
Poor fool, I thought—I should have left a warning.

Some bastard saw my life and thought it nicer
Than what he had. Yet what he'd had seemed fine.
He'd never caught his fingers in the slicer
The way I'd managed in that life of mine.

His life lay glistening in the rain, neglected,
Yet still a decent, an authentic life.
Some people I can think of, I reflected
Would take that thing as soon as you'd say Knife.

It seemed a shame to miss a chance like that.
I brought the life in, dried it by the stove.
It looked so fetching, stretched out on the mat.
I tried it on. It fitted, like a glove.

And now, when some local bat drops off the twig
And new folk take the house, and pull up floors
And knock down walls and hire some kind of big
Container (say, a skip) for their old doors,

I'll watch it like a hawk, and every day
I'll make at least—oh—half a dozen trips.
I've furnished an existence in that way.
You'd not believe the things you find on skips.

JAMES FENTON

NOT WAVING BUT DROWNING

Nobody heard him, the dead man,
But still he lay moaning:
I was much further out than you thought
And not waving but drowning.

Poor chap, he always loved larking
And now he's dead
It must have been too cold for him his heart gave way,
They said.

Oh, no no no no, it was too cold always
(Still the dead one lay moaning)
I was much too far out all my life
And not waving but drowning.

STEVIE SMITH

WORKSHOP

TALKING AND WRITING

Several of the poems in this section ask and attempt to answer the question posed by Sir Walter Raleigh, 'What is our Life?' If life has a purpose, whose purpose is it and what might it be? Raleigh, 400 years ago, compared our brief existence to a performance on stage (p. 43).

- What might be appropriate images for life at the turn of the millennium – the internet, a motorway journey, a flight, a film, a TV soap opera?

- Look carefully at the images in Raleigh's poem. If you have an idea for a modern 'What is our Life?', try to develop it into a poem, beginning with Raleigh's question.

- 'A Consumer's Report' (pp. 42–43) gives one sort of modern answer to Raleigh's question. Hear the poem read aloud (the text could be divided between several voices) and talk about how Peter Porter develops the idea of this 'product' called 'LIFE'. Try writing your own Consumer's Report about the 'competitive product' that is referred to in the last line.

- The four poems on pp. 43–46 ('What is our Life', 'Upon a Dead Man's Head', 'To Daffodils', and 'Sic Vita') were all written in the sixteenth and seventeenth centuries when life expectancy was much shorter than nowadays. Death was an ever-present threat, and a belief in God and the after-life was the norm. Hear the poems read aloud.
   — Discuss the images and the form of each poem (see Part A, Units 3, 4 and 6).
   — Choose *one* poem and write a short account of the ideas and feelings it carries and the images and form it uses to express them.

LIVING A 'GOOD LIFE'

Rudyard Kipling's 'If' (p. 47) is an exhortation to the young men of the British Empire to show 'guts' in the face of adversity.

- List the principles it puts forward for living a good life. Are they still valid today?

PERFORMANCES

Two poems especially lend themselves to performances where you treat the text as a script to be presented to the rest of the class.

- 'A Consumer's Report' (pp. 42–43) can be done as a group reading for three or four voices. Plan where the breaks should come and rehearse your reading.

- '*You will be hearing from us shortly*' (p. 48) can be performed as a rather one-sided interview. How will you deal with the responses on the right?

SEA SYMBOLS

- 'Neither out Far nor in Deep' (p. 46), 'Sitting Sideways to the Sea' (p. 46) and 'Not Waving but Drowning' (p. 51) all use the imagery of the sea and the beach for more than mere description. Hear the poems read aloud.
   — What are the predicaments or positions of the human figures in the three poems and what ideas do they symbolise?
   — Write a comparison of the three poems saying which you prefer and why.

SATIRES AND OPINIONS

TERRIBLE WORLD

I've seen streets of blood
Redda dan red
There waz no luv
Just bodies dead
And I think to myself
What a terrible world.

I've seen pimps and priests
Well interfused
Denying peace
To the kids they abuse
And I think to myself
What a terrible world.

The killer who's the hero
The rapist who's indoors
The trade in human cargo
And dead poets on tours
I've seen friends put in jail
For not being rich
And mass graves made
From a football pitch.

I've seen babies scream
Nobody cared
Civilians starve
Whilst troops are prepared
And I think to myself
What a terrible world
Yes I think to myself
What a terrible world.

BENJAMIN ZEPHANIAH

I do love Louis Armstrong's work but I
thought I should walk the same road and see
things from a different point of view.

MEDITATIO

When I carefully consider the
curious habits of dogs
I am compelled to conclude
That man is the superior animal.

When I consider the curious
habits of man
I confess, my friend, I am
puzzled.

EZRA POUND

next to of course god america i

'next to of course god america i
love you land of the pilgrims' and so forth oh
say can you see by the dawn's early my
country 'tis of centuries come and go
and are no more what of it we should worry
in every language even deafanddumb
thy sons acclaim your glorious name by gorry
by jingo by gee by gosh by gum
why talk of beauty what could be more beautiful than these heroic happy dead
who rushed like lions to the roaring slaughter
they did not stop to think they died instead
then shall the voice of liberty be mute?'

He spoke. And drank rapidly a glass of water

e.e. cummings

ONCE UPON A TIME

Once upon a time, son,
they used to laugh with their hearts
and laugh with their eyes;
but now they only laugh with their teeth,
while their ice-block-cold eyes
search behind my shadow.

There was a time indeed
they used to shake hands with their hearts;
but that's gone, son.
Now they shake hands without hearts
while their left hands search
my empty pockets.

'Feel at home,' 'Come again,'
they say, and when I come
again and feel
at home, once, twice,
there will be no thrice—
for then I find doors shut on me.

So I have learned many things, son.
I have learned to wear many faces
like dresses—homeface,
officeface, streetface, hostface, cock-
tailface, with all their conforming smiles
like a fixed portrait smile.

And I have learned too
to laugh with only my teeth
and shake hands without my heart.
I have also learned to say, 'Goodbye,'
when I mean 'Goodriddance';
to say 'Glad to meet you,'
without being glad; and to say 'It's been
nice talking to you,' after being bored.

But believe me, son.
I want to be what I used to be
when I was like you. I want
to unlearn all these muting things.
Most of all, I want to relearn
how to laugh, for my laugh in the mirror
shows only my teeth like a snake's bare fangs!

So show me, son,
how to laugh; show me how
I used to laugh and smile
once upon a time when I was like you.

GABRIEL OKARA

BLACK

Show me the woman
that would surrender
her little black dress
to a white-robed clan
and I would show you a liar.

Not for their bonfire,
her wardrobe saviour
the number
in which she comes
into her own power.

Go to a funeral
in black and know
that the dead
beside the white candles
will not be offended.

Add amber earrings,
perhaps a hat or scarf of pink
and know you are ready—
for a wedding.
How black absorbs everything.

Stand around at a party
in black—you are your own artist,
your own sensual catalyst,
surprised to say the least
when black brings you

Those sudden inexplicable hostile glances.

GRACE NICHOLS

TELEPHONE CONVERSATION

The price seemed reasonable, location
Indifferent. The landlady swore she lived
Off premises. Nothing remained
But self-confession. 'Madam,' I warned,
'I hate a wasted journey—I am African.'
Silence. Silenced transmission of
Pressurized good-breeding. Voice, when it came,
Lipstick coated, long gold-rolled
Cigarette-holder pipped. Caught I was, foully.
'HOW DARK?' . . . I had not misheard . . . 'ARE YOU LIGHT
OR VERY DARK?' Button B. Button A. Stench
Of rancid breath of public hide-and-speak.
Red booth. Red pillar-box. Red double-tiered
Omnibus squelching tar. It *was* real! Shamed
By ill-mannered silence, surrender
Pushed dumbfounded to beg simplification.
Considerate she was, varying the emphasis—
'ARE YOU DARK? OR VERY LIGHT?' Revelation came.
'You mean—like plain or milk chocolate?'
Her assent was clinical, crushing in its light
Impersonality. Rapidly, wave-length adjusted,
I chose. 'West African sepia'—and as afterthought,
'Down in my passport.' Silence for spectroscopic
Flight of fancy, till truthfulness clanged her accent
Hard on the mouthpiece. 'WHAT'S THAT?' conceding
'DON'T KNOW WHAT THAT IS.' 'Like brunette.'
'THAT'S DARK, ISN'T IT?' 'Not altogether.
Facially, I am brunette, but madam, you should see
The rest of me. Palm of my hand, soles of my feet
Are a peroxide blonde. Friction, caused—
Foolishly madam—by sitting down, has turned
My bottom raven black—One moment madam!'—sensing
Her receiver rearing on the thunderclap
About my ears—'Madam,' I pleaded, 'wouldn't you rather
See for yourself?'

WOLE SOYINKA

NEIGHBOURS

I am the type you are supposed to fear
Black and foreign
Big and dreadlocks
An uneducated grass eater.

I talk in tongues
I chant at night
I appear anywhere,
I sleep with lions
And when the moon gets me
I am a Wailer.

I am moving in
Next door to you
So you can get to know me,
You will see my shadow
In the bathroom window,
My aromas will occupy
Your space,
Our ball will be in your court.
How will you feel?

You should feel good
You have been chosen.

I am the type you are supposed to love
Dark and mysterious
Tall and natural
Thinking, tea total.
I talk in schools
I sing on TV
I am in the papers,
I keep cool cats

And when the sun is shining
I go Carnival.

BENJAMIN ZEPHANIAH

LISTEN MR OXFORD DON

Me not no Oxford don
me a simple immigrant
from Clapham Common
I didn't graduate
I immigrate

But listen Mr Oxford don
I'm a man on de run
and a man on de run
is a dangerous one

I ent have no gun
I ent have no knife
but mugging de Queen's English
is the story of my life

I dont need no axe
to split/ up yu syntax
I dont need no hammer
to mash/ up yu grammar

I warning you Mr Oxford don
I'm a wanted man
and a wanted man
is a dangerous one

Dem accuse me of assault
on de Oxford dictionary/
imagine a concise peaceful man like me/
dem want me serve time
for inciting rhyme to riot
but I tekking it quiet
down here in Clapham Common

I'm not a violent man Mr Oxford don
I only armed wit mih human breath
but human breath
is a dangerous weapon

So mek dem send one big word after me
I ent serving no jail sentence
I slashing suffix in self-defence
I bashing future wit present tense
and if necessary

I making de Queen's English accessory/to my offence

JOHN AGARD

NO DIALECTS PLEASE

In this competition
dey was lookin for poetry of worth
for a writin that could wrap up a feelin
an fling it back hard
with a captive power to choke de stars
so dey say,
'Send them to us
but NO DIALECTS PLEASE'
We're British!

Ay!
Well ah laugh till me boushet near drop
Is not only dat ah tink
of de dialect of de Normans and de Saxons
dat combine an reformulate
to create a language-elect
is not only dat ah tink
how dis British education must really be narrow
if it leave dem wid no knowledge
of what dey own history is about
is not only dat ah tink
bout de part of my story
dat come from Liverpool in a big dirty white ship
mark
AFRICAN SLAVES PLEASE!
We're the British!

But as if dat not enough pain
for a body to bear
ah tink bout de part on de plantations down dere
Wey dey so frighten o de power
in the deep spaces
behind our watching faces
dat dey shout
NO AFRICAN LANGUAGES PLEASE!
It's against the law!
Make me ha to go
an start up a language o me own
dat ah could share wid me people
Den when we start to shout
bout a culture o we own
a language o we own
a identity o we own
dem an de others dey leave to control us say
STOP THAT NONSENSE NOW
We're all British!
Every time we lif we foot to do we own ting
to fight we own fight
dey tell us how British we British
an ah wonder if dey remember
dat in Trinidad in the thirties

dey jail Butler
who dey say is their British citizen
an accuse him of
Hampering the war effort!
Then it was
FIGHT FOR YOUR COUNTRY, FOLKS!
You're British!
Ay! Ay!
Ah wonder when it change to
NO DIALECTS PLEASE!
WE'RE British!
Huh!
To tink how still dey so dunce
an so frighten o we power
dat dey have to hide behind a language
that we could wrap roun we little finger
in addition to we own!
Heavens o mercy!
Dat is dunceness oui!
Ah wonder where is de bright British?

MERLE COLLINS

A GREEN SONG

to sing at the bottle-bank

One green bottle,
Drop it in the bank.
Ten green bottles,
What a lot we drank.
Heaps of bottles
And yesterday's a blank
But we'll save the planet,
Tinkle, tinkle, clank!

We've got bottles—
Nice, percussive trash.
Bags of bottles,
We love to hear them smash
And we'll save the planet,
Tinkle, tinkle, crash!

WENDY COPE

FROM THE MOTORWAY

Everywhere up and down the island
Britain is mending her desert.
Marvellous, we exclaim as we fly on it,
tying the country in a parcel.
London to Edinburgh, Birmingham to Cardiff,
no time to examine the contents,

thank you, but consider the bliss
of sitting absolutely numbed to your
nulled mind, music when you want it,
while identical miles thunder under you,
the same spot coming and going
seventy, eighty times a minute,

till you're there, wherever there
is, ready to be someone in
Liverpool, Leeds, Manchester,
they're all the same to the road,
which loves itself, which nonetheless
here and there hands you trailing

necklaces of fume in which to be
one squeezed breather among
rich and ragged, sprinter and staggerer,
a status parade for Major Roadworks
toiling in his red-trimmed triangle,
then a regiment of wounded orange witches

defending a shamelessly naked
(rarely a stitch of work on her)
captive free lane,
while the inchlings inch on
without bite or sup, at most
a hard-shoulder to creep on,

while there, on all sides,
lie your unwrapped destinations,
lanes trickling off into childhood
or anonymity, apple-scented villages
asleep in their promise of being
nowhere anyone would like to get to.

ANNE STEVENSON

GARDENERS' QUESTION TIME

Well, after lagging your tubers
nest them deep in the airing-cupboard.
If you cadge your wife's old vest
it snugs 'em down lovely,
you'll get interest on your warmth in May.

Shallots, the wardrobe: my great-uncle
would entertain no other store.
In the darkness, festoon them on hangers,
you'll have to evict the wife's hats
but you'll be munching on plumpness in May.

A pair of knickers strains barrel-water
best, and I'll say something else:
if you can borrow your wife's bra
it's a smashing cradle to ripen peaches,
trembling on the washing-line in June,

scarcely reining their softness, for you.
As for mulch, there's nothing matches
blood & bone. If she's dead lately,
put your wife through the shredder,
(ask her first) and scatter it thick.

You'll be in that deckchair in August,
lungs full of lush green peace,
just you, your life, and the shed. Heaven.

STEVE ELLIS

WORKSHOP

WONDERFUL WORLD?

The poem 'Terrible World' (p. 53) is a parody of the classic song 'Wonderful World' by the great, black jazz musician Louis Armstrong. 'Wonderful World' is very positive and optimistic in tone:

> I see trees of green
> Red roses too
> I see them bloom
> For me and you
> And I think to myself
> What a wonderful world.

The contemporary black poet Benjamin Zephaniah turns the wonderful world of Armstrong's song upside down as he points to some of the appalling truths about the world today.

● There may be something you personally feel strongly about which is not included in Zephaniah's poem such as crime, drugs, animal rights, racial abuse, homelessness, religious intolerance, torture—sadly, the list is endless. Write your own verse on the same pattern and rhyme scheme as the opening verses of Terrible/Wonderful World:

> I see .... *a*
> .... *b*
> .... *c*
> .... *b*
> And I think to myself
> What a terrible world

● If you feel you have enough ideas, write further verses to the same pattern. You could join with others in making a class poem to which several people contribute verses.

● If you are of a more optimistic turn of mind, you could point to more positive ideas and create a 'Wonderful World' poem of your own which celebrates the things you think are good about being alive. Display the results side by side.

BLACK, WHITE, STEREOTYPE

In the poem 'Neighbours' (p. 58), Benjamin Zephaniah initially plays on the white person's negative stereotype of 'the type you are supposed to fear / Black and foreign . . .' and then reverses the situation by saying that he is also 'the type you are supposed to love' and points out that he belongs to another positive stereotype also— 'Dark and mysterious / Tall and natural / Thinking, tea total' who gives talks in schools, appears on TV and in the papers and is a cat lover.

● Take up the position of somebody who makes others uncomfortable in society and about whom people often feel prejudice: somebody of a particular religion; somebody who is disabled in some way; somebody who is mentally ill; the beggar in the street, for example—and write your own piece beginning 'I am the type you are supposed to fear' or 'I am the type you are supposed to pity'. List the negative things that people fear and then find a positive list to counterbalance this.

Many years ago, when studying at university in England, the black Nigerian poet Wole Soyinka wrote a poem about his experience of trying to find lodgings. His poem 'Telephone Conversation' (p. 57) was the result.

- In pairs, with one playing the part of the writer and the other the part of the landlady work out a performance of the poem.

Soyinka, poet, playwright, novelist has since gone on to win the Nobel Prize for literature – the highest accolade the world can bestow upon a writer. Would that cut much ice with his landlady?

Merle Collins is another Caribbean writer who is all too aware of the ironies of being black British. In her poem 'No Dialects Please' (p. 59) the language in which she chooses to write is the English dialect of her Caribbean heritage but this is unacceptable to those who run the poetry competition she is thinking of entering. She is appalled and amazed at the ignorance and the fear that underlie this attitude particularly when, in time of need, her people have been assured that they are, of course, British.

Language is central to personal and cultural identity as John Agard wittily recognises in his poem 'Listen Mr Oxford Don' (p. 58). As he states 'I only armed wit me human breath / but human breath / is a dangerous weapon'.

- Read these two poems and discuss what it is about language that make people fear difference and what makes others want to standardise it, ironing out any dialects.
- It isn't just a Caribbean/Standard English division. You may find it helpful to link these poems with the Scots poet Liz Lochhead's poem 'Kidspoem/Bairnsang' on p. 205.

PERFORMANCES

Many of the poems in this section are ideal for performing in pairs or small groups. It is possible to take a set of poems that are linked in some way and to make a tape recording of them.

- 'A Green Song (*to sing at the bottle-bank*)' (p. 60) is a typically subversive poem by Wendy Cope. Try to sing it to the tune of 'Ten Green Bottles'.
- 'Gardeners' Question Time' by Steve Ellis (p. 61) has to be heard as a performance. It needs the rich, loamy tones of those evocatively named garden experts on radio and television—Sowerbutts, Flowerdew, Loads, Clay Jones and the rest. You could try a performance with three or four 'expert' voices each taking a section of the poem and offering their timely advice.
- Choose one or two other poems and then rehearse and record your tape.

PATRIOTIC PATTER

e.e. cummings' poem on p. 55 with the odd title 'next to of course god america i' contains in almost every line a cliché of the kind so often spouted by politicians. The clichés are nearly all drawn from patriotic songs, speeches and verse and are crammed together in a mad jumble, only stopping at the next to last line. The whole inflated balloon is then punctured.

- In pairs, make a list of any similar clichés you might find in newspaper headlines, political speeches, rousing songs and so forth . . . 'Land of . . .' 'We must tighten our belts . . .' 'We must all pull together . . .' 'This great party of ours . . .'. Join forces with another pair if you need more ideas.
- Now try to run the clichés together into a series of lines that appear to make some kind of sense.

W A R

THE SOLDIER'S DEATH

Trail all your pikes, dispirit every drum,
March in a slow procession from afar,
Ye silent, ye dejected men of war!
Be still the hautboys, and the flute be dumb!
Display no more, in vain, the lofty banner.
For see! where on the bier* before ye lies
The pale, the fall'n, th' untimely sacrifice
To your mistaken shrine, to your false idol Honour.

ANNE, COUNTESS OF WINCHELSEA (1661–1720)
★ stretcher

THE CHARGE OF THE LIGHT BRIGADE

Half a league, half a league,
  Half a league onward,
All in the valley of Death
  Rode the six hundred.
'Forward the Light Brigade!
Charge for the guns!' he said:
Into the valley of Death
  Rode the six hundred.

'Forward the Light Brigade!'
Was there a man dismay'd?
Not tho' the soldier knew
  Some one had blunder'd:
Their's not to make reply,
Their's not to reason why,
Their's but to do and die:
Into the valley of Death
  Rode the six hundred.

Cannon to right of them,
Cannon to left of them,
Cannon in front of them
  Volley'd and thunder'd;
Storm'd at with shot and shell,
Boldly they rode and well,
Into the jaws of Death,
Into the mouth of Hell,
  Rode the six hundred.

Flash'd all their sabres bare,
Flash'd as they turn'd in air,
Sabring the gunners there,
Charging an army, while
  All the world wonder'd:

Plunged in the battery-smoke
Right thro' the line they broke;
Cossack and Russian
Reel'd from the sabre-stroke
  Shatter'd and sunder'd.
Then they rode back, but not,
  Not the six hundred.

Cannon to right of them,
Cannon to left of them,
Cannon behind them
  Volley'd and thunder'd;
Storm'd at with shot and shell,
While horse and hero fell,
They that had fought so well
Came thro' the jaws of Death
Back from the mouth of Hell,
All that was left of them,
  Left of six hundred.

When can their glory fade?
O the wild charge they made!
  All the world wonder'd.
Honour the charge they made!
Honour the Light Brigade,
  Noble six hundred!

LORD TENNYSON (1809–1892)

The Light Brigade were ordered by Lord Lucan to charge
12,000 Russians, who were fully prepared with artillery to receive them:
247 out of 673 officers and men were killed. Tennyson based his poem
on *The Times* report which included the words, 'some one had
blunder'd'.

TOMMY[1]

I went into a public-'ouse to get a pint o'beer,
The publican 'e up an' sez, 'We serve no red-coats here.'
The girls be'ind the bar they laughed an' giggled fit to die,
I outs into the street again an' to myself sez I:
      O it's Tommy this, an' Tommy that, an' 'Tommy, go away';
      But it's 'Thank you, Mister Atkins,' when the band begins to play—
      The band begins to play, my boys, the band begins to play,
      O it's 'Thank you, Mister Atkins,' when the band begins to play.

I went into a theatre as sober as could be,
They gave a drunk civilian room, but 'adn't none for me;
They sent me to the gallery[2] or round the music-'alls,
But when it comes to fightin', Lord! they'll shove me in the stalls!
      For it's Tommy this, an' Tommy that, an' 'Tommy, wait outside';
      But its 'Special train for Atkins' when the trooper's on the tide—
      The troopship's on the tide, my boys, the troopship's on the tide,
      O it's 'Special train for Atkins' when the trooper's on the tide.

Yes, makin' mock o' uniforms that guard you while you sleep
Is cheaper than them uniforms, an' they're starvation cheap;
An' hustlin' drunken soldiers when they're goin' large a bit
Is five times better business than paradin' in full kit.
      Then it's Tommy this, an' Tommy that, an' 'Tommy, 'ow's yer soul?'
      But it's 'Thin red line of 'eroes'[3] when the drums begin to roll—
      The drums begin to roll, my boys, the drums begin to roll,
      O it's 'Thin red line of 'eroes' when the drums begin to roll.

We aren't no thin red 'eroes, nor we aren't no blackguards too,
But single men in barricks, most remarkable like you;
An' if sometimes our conduck isn't all your fancy paints,
Why, single men in barricks don't grow into plaster saints;
      While it's Tommy this, an' Tommy that, an' 'Tommy, fall be'ind,'
      But it's 'Please to walk in front, sir,' when there's trouble in the wind—
      There's trouble in the wind, my boys, there's trouble in the wind,
      O it's 'Please to walk in front, sir,' when there's trouble in the wind.

You talk o' better food for us, an' schools, an' fires, an' all:
We'll wait for extry rations if you treat us rational.
Don't mess about the cook-room slops, but prove it to our face
The Widow's Uniform[4] is not the soldier-man's disgrace.
      For it's Tommy this, an' Tommy that, an' 'Chuck him out, the brute!'
      But it's 'Saviour of 'is country' when the guns begin to shoot;
      An' it's Tommy this, an' Tommy that, an' anything you please;
      An' Tommy ain't a bloomin' fool—you bet that Tommy sees!

RUDYARD KIPLING (1865–1936)

[1] Derived from 'Thomas Atkins,' as the typical name for a soldier in the British army.
[2] Cheaper seats in a theatre, in the balcony; the best seats, downstairs, are the stalls.
[3] The phrase 'thin red line tipped with steel' was used by *The Times* to describe the 93rd Highlanders infantry regiment as they stood to meet the advancing Russian cavalry at Balaclava (1854), in the Crimean War.
[4] Kipling occasionally referred to Queen Victoria as 'The Widow at Windsor.'

THE REAR-GUARD

(Hindenburg Line, April 1917)

Groping along the tunnel, step by step,
He winked his prying torch with patching glare
From side to side, and sniffed the unwholesome air.

Tins, boxes, bottles, shapes too vague to know;
A mirror smashed, the mattress from a bed;
And he, exploring fifty feet below
The rosy gloom of battle overhead.

Tripping, he grabbed the wall; saw some one lie
Humped at his feet, half-hidden by a rug,
And stooped to give the sleeper's arm a tug.
'I'm looking for headquarters.' No reply.
'God blast your neck!' (For days he'd had no sleep,)
'Get up and guide me through this stinking place.'

Savage, he kicked a soft, unanswering heap,
And flashed his beam across the livid face
Terribly glaring up, whose eyes yet wore
Agony dying hard ten days before;
And fists of fingers clutched a blackening wound.

Alone he staggered on until he found
Dawn's ghost that filtered down a shafted stair
To the dazed, muttering creatures underground
Who hear the boom of shells in muffled sound.
At last, with sweat of horror in his hair,
He climbed through darkness to the twilight air,
Unloading hell behind him step by step.

SIEGFRIED SASSOON

THE HERO

'Jack fell as he'd have wished,' the Mother said,
And folded up the letter that she'd read.
'The Colonel writes so nicely.' Something broke
In the tired voice that quavered to a choke.
She half looked up. 'We mothers are so proud
Of our dead soldiers.' Then her face was bowed.

Quietly the Brother Officer went out.
He'd told the poor old dear some gallant lies
That she would nourish all her days, no doubt.
For while he coughed and mumbled, her weak eyes
Had shone with gentle triumph, brimmed with joy,
Because he'd been so brave, her glorious boy.

He thought how 'Jack', cold-footed, useless swine,
Had panicked down the trench that night the mine
Went up at Wicked Corner; how he'd tried
To get sent home, and how, at last, he died,
Blown to small bits. And no one seemed to care
Except that lonely woman with white hair.

SIEGFRIED SASSOON

DULCE ET DECORUM EST

Bent double, like old beggars under sacks,
Knock-kneed, coughing like hags, we cursed through sludge,
Till on the haunting flares we turned our backs,
And towards our distant rest began to trudge.
Men marched asleep. Many had lost their boots,
But limped on, blood-shod. All went lame, all blind;
Drunk with fatigue; deaf even to the hoots
Of gas-shells dropping softly behind.

Gas! GAS! Quick, boys!—An ecstasy of fumbling,
Fitting the clumsy helmets just in time,
But someone still was yelling out and stumbling
And floundering like a man in fire or lime.—
Dim through the misty panes and thick green light,
As under a green sea, I saw him drowning.

In all my dreams before my helpless sight
He plunges at me, guttering, choking, drowning.

If in some smothering dreams, you too could pace
Behind the wagon that we flung him in,
And watch the white eyes writhing in his face,
His hanging face, like a devil's sick of sin;
If you could hear at every jolt, the blood
Come gargling from the froth-corrupted lungs,
Bitter as the cud
Of vile, incurable sores on innocent tongues,—
My friend, you would not tell with such high zest
To children ardent for some desperate glory,
The old Lie: *Dulce et decorum est*
Pro patria mori.

WILFRED OWEN

THE VETERAN
May, 1916

We came upon him sitting in the sun,
  Blinded by war, and left. And past the fence
There came young soldiers from the Hand and Flower,
  Asking advice of his experience.

And he said this, and that, and told them tales,
  And all the nightmares of each empty head
Blew into air; then hearing us beside,
  'Poor chaps, how'd they know what it's like?' he said.

And we stood there, and watched him as he sat,
  Turning his sockets where they went away,
Until it came to one of us to ask
  'And you're—how old?'
        'Nineteen, the third of May.'

MARGARET POSTGATE COLE

THE SOLDIER

If I should die, think only this of me:
   That there's some corner of a foreign field
That is for ever England. There shall be
   In that rich earth a richer dust concealed;
A dust whom England bore, shaped, made aware,
   Gave, once, her flowers to love, her ways to roam,
A body of England's, breathing English air,
   Washed by the rivers, blest by suns of home.

And think, this heart, all evil shed away,
   A pulse in the eternal mind, no less
      Gives somewhere back the thoughts by England given;
Her sights and sounds; dreams happy as her day;
   And laughter, learnt of friends; and gentleness,
      In hearts at peace, under an English heaven.

RUPERT BROOKE

CHRISTMAS: 1924

'Peace upon earth!' was said. We sing it,
And pay a million priests to bring it.
After two thousand years of mass
We've got as far as poison gas.

THOMAS HARDY

HIGH WOOD

Ladies and gentlemen, this is High Wood,
Called by the French, Bois des Fourneaux,
The famous spot which in Nineteen-Sixteen,
July, August and September was the scene
Of long and bitterly contested strife,
By reason of its high commanding site.
Observe the effect of shell-fire in the trees.
Standing and fallen; here is wire; this trench
For months inhabited, twelve times changed hands;
(They soon fall in), used later as a grave.
It has been said on good authority
That in the fighting for this patch of wood
Were killed somewhere above eight thousand men,
Of whom the greater part were buried here,
This mound on which you stand being . . .
                                    Madame, please,
You are requested kindly not to touch
Or take away the Company's property
As souvenirs; you'll find we have on sale
A large variety, all guaranteed.
As I was saying, all is as it was,
This is an unknown British officer,
The tunic having lately rotted off.
Please follow me—this way . . .
                    the *path*, sir, *please*,
The ground which was secured at great expense
The Company keeps absolutely untouched,
And in that dug-out (genuine) we provide
Refreshments at a reasonable rate.
You are requested not to leave about
Paper, or ginger-beer bottles, or orange-peel,
There are waste-paper baskets at the gate.

PHILIP JOHNSTONE

from: DUNKIRK

All through the night, and in the next day's light
The endless columns came. Here was Defeat.
The men marched doggedly, and kept their arms,
But sleep weighed on their backs so that they reeled,
Staggering as they passed. Their force was spent.
Only, like old Horatius, each man saw
Far off his home, and seeing, plodded on.
At last they ceased. The sun shone down, and we
Were left to watch along a dusty road.

That night we blew our guns. We placed a shell
Fuze downwards in each muzzle. Then we put
Another in the breech, secured a wire
Fast to the firing lever, crouched, and pulled.
It sounded like a cry of agony,
The crash and clang of splitting, tempered steel.
Thus did our guns, our treasured colours, pass;
And we were left bewildered, weaponless,
And rose and marched, our faces to the sea.

We formed in line beside the water's edge.
The little waves made oddly home-like sounds,
Breaking in half-seen surf upon the strand.
The night was full of noise; the whistling thud
The shells made in the sand, and pattering stones;
The cries cut short, the shouts of units' names;
The crack of distant shots, and bren gun fire;
The sudden clattering crash of masonry.
Steadily, all the time, the marching tramp
Of feet passed by along the shell-torn road,
Under the growling thunder of the guns.

The major said 'The boats cannot get in,
'There is no depth of water. Follow me.'
And so we followed, wading in our ranks
Into the blackness of the sea. And there,
Lit by the burning oil across the swell,
We stood and waited for the unseen boats.

Oars in the darkness, rowlocks, shadowy shapes
Of boats that searched. We heard a seaman's hail.
Then we swam out, and struggled with our gear,
Clutching the looming gunwales. Strong hands pulled,
And we were in and heaving with the rest,
Until at last they turned. The dark oars dipped,
The laden craft crept slowly out to sea,
To where in silence lay the English ships.

B.G. BONALLACK May/June 1940

LUCK

I suppose they'll say his last thoughts were of simple things,
Of April back at home, and the late sun on his wings;
Or that he murmured someone's name
As earth reclaimed him sheathed in flame.
Oh God! Let's have no more of empty words,
Lip service ornamenting death!
The worms don't spare the hero;
Nor can children feed upon resounding praises of his deed.
'He died who loved to live,' they'll say,
'Unselfishly so we might have today!'
Like hell! He fought because he had to fight;
He died that's all. It was his unlucky night.

DENNIS McHARRIE

BEACH BURIAL

Softly and humbly to the Gulf of Arabs
The convoys of dead soldiers come;
At night they sway and wander in the waters far under,
But morning rolls them in the foam.

Between the sob and clubbing of the gunfire
Someone, it seems, has time for this,
To pluck them from the shallows and bury them in burrows
And tread the sand upon their nakedness;

And each cross, the driven stake of tidewood,
Bears the last signature of men,
Written with such perplexity, with such bewildered pity,
The words choke as they begin—

'Unknown seaman'—the ghostly pencil
Wavers and fades, the purple drips,
The breath of the wet season has washed their inscriptions
As blue as drowned men's lips,

Dead seamen, gone in search of the same landfall,
Whether as enemies they fought,
Or fought with us, or neither; the sand joins them together,
Enlisted on the other front.

El Alamein 1944

KENNETH SLESSOR

THE RESPONSIBILITY

I am the man who gives the word,
If it should come, to use the Bomb.

I am the man who spreads the word
From him to them if it should come.

I am the man who gets the word
From him who spreads the word from him.

I am the man who drops the Bomb
If ordered by the one who's heard
From him who merely spreads the word
The first one gives if it should come.

I am the man who loads the Bomb
That he must drop should orders come
From him who gets the word passed on
By one who waits to hear from *him*.

I am the man who makes the Bomb
That he must load for him to drop
If told by one who gets the word
From one who passes it from *him*.

I am the man who fills the till,
Who pays the tax, who foots the bill
That guarantees the Bomb he makes
For him to load for him to drop
If orders come from one who gets
The word passed on to him by one
Who waits to hear it from the man
Who gives the word to use the Bomb.

I am the man behind it all;
I am the one responsible.

PETER APPLETON

RELATIVE SADNESS

Einstein's eyes
were filled with tears
when he heard about Hiroshima.
Mr. Tamihi
had no eyes left
to show his grief.

COLIN ROWBOTHAM

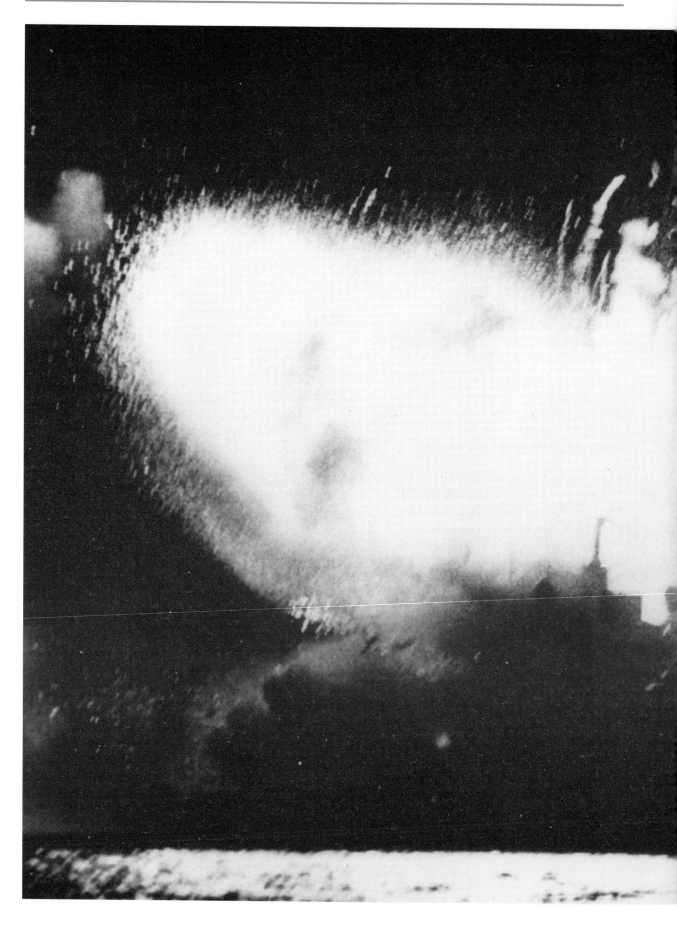

THREE WEEKS TO ARGENTINA

Shall I wave my little
Union Jack?
Shall I go all out for
a big attack?
Shall I sing: 'My country
right or wrong!'?
Shall I rattle out a
sabre song?

Or shall I write of
sailor boys
deep in the sea, that can
make no noise?
Or of feckless, careless
young marines
missed by the girls
and the wet canteens?

It's hard for an old man,
who's seen wars,
to welcome that devil
and his claws.

They reach from the ocean,
clash in the sky,
make the earth into
a shepherd's pie.

Professionals love it,
the admirals all,
a chance to show that they're
on the ball.
Newsmen like it,
because it's news—
but fathers and mothers
have different views.

GAVIN EWART (17 April 1982)

STRIKING DISTANCE

Was there one moment when the woman
who's always lived next door turned stranger
to you? In a time of fearful weather,
did the way she laughed, or shook out her mats
make you suddenly feel as though
she'd been nursing a dark side to her difference,
and bring that word, in a bitter rush
to the back of the throat—*Croat/Muslim/*
Serb—the name, barbed, ripping
its neat solution through common ground?

Or has she acquired an alien patina
day by uneasy day, unnoticed
as fall-out from a remote explosion?
So you don't know quite when you came to think
the way she sits, or ties her scarf,
is just like a Muslim/Serb/Croat;
and she uses their word for water-melon
as usual, but now it's an irritant
you mimic to ugliness in your head,
surprising yourself in a savage pleasure.

Do you sometimes think, she could be you,
the woman who's trying to be invisible?
Do you have to betray those old complicities
—money worries, sick children, men?
Would an open door be too much pain
if the larger bravery is beyond you
(you can't afford the kind of recklessness
that would take, any more than she could);
while your husband is saying you don't understand
those people/Serbs/Muslims/Croats?

One morning, will you ignore her greeting
and think you see a strange twist to her smile
—for how could she not, then, be strange to herself
(this woman who lives nine inches away)
in the inner place where she'd felt she belonged,
which, now, she'll return to obsessively
as a tongue tries to limit a secret sore?
And as they drive her away, will her face
be unfamiliar, her voice, bearable:
a woman crying from a long way off?

CAROLE SATYAMURTI

WORKSHOP

PERFORMANCES

The poems in this section are presented in historical sequence, beginning with an eighteenth-century woman writer's reaction to the soldiers' 'false idol Honour' and ending with Carole Satyamurti's questioning poem about the Bosnian war. In between, you can read different poets' reactions to some of the major conflicts of the last 150 years.

In pairs/small groups

● Produce a performance or taped programme on the theme of War, linking some of these poems together, perhaps with a commentary. Below are a few ideas to start you thinking.

The Crimean War 1853–56

—This war between Russia and the allied powers of Turkey, Britain and France is largely remembered, in Britain at least, for two things: the heroic nursing reforms of Florence Nightingale and the futile slaughter of a brigade of British cavalry who, due to a confusion of orders, charged some entrenched, well-prepared batteries of Russian artillery. Tennyson's famous poem 'The Charge of the Light Brigade' (p. 64) is a patriotic response by the then Poet Laureate to the news of this disaster. In contrast, Kipling's 'Tommy' (p. 65), written a generation later (with the Crimean War in recent memory, and with Queen Victoria still reigning over the British Empire), gives a view from the ranks of the sharply differing experiences of the soldier's life in peace time and in war.

Prepare your readings of these poems to bring out the contrast in their feelings and messages.

World War One 1914–18

—Several of the poems in this section are written as tiny dramatic scenes. Sassoon's poems 'The Rear-Guard' and 'The Hero' on p. 66 are both powerful dramatic evocations of incidents from the horrific trench warfare. Rehearse readings of these poems using different voices for the different parts.

—Hardy's bitter comment in his poem 'Christmas: 1924' (p. 70) is a reminder of the horrors of poison gas which was used extensively in trench warfare. It provides a fitting link to a dramatised reading of Owen's description of a mustard gas attack in his poem 'Dulce et Decorum Est' on p. 67. The latin phrase which is the title of the poem and which ends it is often to be found carved on war memorials. It means 'It is sweet and right to die for one's country'.

—Rupert Brooke's poem 'The Soldier' on p. 69 may be read by a single voice as a contrasting view to that of Owen or Sassoon.

—'High Wood' (p. 70) is a poem about a bitterly contested strip of land where 8,000 men fell; it can be read by one person in an unfeeling tour guide's voice.

World War Two 1939–45

—The poems from this war provide some sharp contrasts, including a narrative account of one of the major incidents – the rescue of over 300,000 Allied troops from the beaches near Dunkirk, and a bitter reply to those who 'ornament death' in battle with romantic remarks (pp. 71–72). Each is probably best read by a single voice which aims to get into the character who is speaking and the feelings expressed in the poem. The Second World War ended with the dropping of atom bombs on the Japanese cities of Hiroshima and Nagasaki. The two poems on p. 73 are reminders, not only of this horror, but also that something much worse could be released today at the touch of a button. 'The Responsibility' is built on the same pattern as the children's nursery rhyme, 'This is the House that Jack Built' and it needs to be read by several people, each taking one of the parts and all coming together for the final two lines.

The Falklands War, 1982 and The Bosnian War 1990–
—'Three Weeks in Argentina' (p. 75) and 'Striking Distance' (p. 76) arise out of more recent conflicts. Find out what you can about these wars before you tackle the poems. Both invite shared reading. Gavin Ewart's poem begins with six questions which could be spoken by different voices before the voice of the 'old man' takes over in section three. 'Striking Distance', too, is full of questions: the four verses could be spoken by different readers.

POSTER POEMS

- The recruiting posters on pp. 67–68 were like advertisements for young men to join the army and were to be seen on hoardings everywhere during the First World War.

- What sort of feelings were they appealing to? Discuss your ideas in pairs and share them with the class. Try to write your own poem beginning with the words of one or other of the posters as your first line. Display your finished poem alongside a copy of the poster or devise your own recruiting poster.

RESEARCH AND WRITING

- Talk to older people you know – neighbours, relatives, grandparents – who may have memories of the Second World War and try to build up a picture of what it meant to them and their families.
  You may find it helpful to concentrate on one aspect of the conflict they remember well such as air-raids. What was the first indication of a raid? Did they have shelter? What was it like to be inside waiting and listening? What sounds stick in the memory?

- Jot down notes from your researches, or, better still, tape-record such memories and use them as either a starting point for a piece of your own writing or as other voices you can fit into your taped programme of war poems.

RELIGIOUS EXPERIENCE

THE PILGRIMAGE

I travelled on, seeing the hill, where lay
            My expectation.
        A long it was and weary way.
        The gloomy cave of Desperation
I left on the one, and on the other side
            The rock of Pride.

And so I came to fancy's meadow strowed
            With many a flower:
        Fain would I here have made abode,
        But I was quickened by my hour.
So to care's copse I came, and there got through
            With much ado.

That led me to the wild of passion, which
            Some call the wold;
        A wasted place, but sometimes rich.
        Here I was robbed of all my gold,
Save one good Angel, which a friend had tied
            Close to my side.

At length I got unto the gladsome hill,
            Where lay my hope,
        Where lay my heart; and climbing still,
        When I had gained the brow and top,
A lake of brackish waters on the ground
            Was all I found.

With that abashed and struck with many a sting
            Of swarming fears,
        I fell and cried, Alas my King;
        Can both the way and end be tears?
Yet taking heart I rose, and then perceived
            I was deceived;

My hill was further: so I flung away,
            Yet heard a cry
        Just as I went, *None goes that way*
        And lives: if that be all, said I,
After so foul a journey death is fair,
            And but a chair.

GEORGE HERBERT (1593–1633)

REDEMPTION

Having been tenant long to a rich Lord,
    Not thriving, I resolved to be bold,
    And make a suit unto him, to afford
A new small-rented lease, and cancell th' old.
In heaven at his manour I him sought:
    They told me there, that he was lately gone
    About some land, which he had dearly bought
Long since on earth, to take possession.
I straight return'd, and knowing his great birth,
    Sought him accordingly in great resorts;
    In cities, theatres, gardens, parks, and courts:
At length I heard a ragged noise and mirth
    Of theeves and murderers: there I him espied,
    Who straight, *Your suit is granted*, said, & died.

GEORGE HERBERT (1593–1633)

PREPARATIONS

Yet if His Majesty, our sovereign lord,
Should of his own accord
Friendly himself invite,
And say 'I'll be your guest to-morrow night,'
How should we stir ourselves, call and command
All hands to work! 'Let no man idle stand!
'Set me fine Spanish tables in the hall;
See they be fitted all;
Let there be room to eat
And order taken that there want no meat.
See every sconce and candlestick made bright,
That without tapers they may give a light.

'Look to the presence: are the carpets spread,
The dazie o'er the head,
The cushions in the chairs,
And all the candles lighted on the stairs?
Perfume the chambers, and in any case
Let each man give attendance in his place!'
Thus, if the king were coming, would we do;
And 'twere good reason too;
For 'tis a duteous thing
To show all honour to an earthly king,
And after all our travail and our cost,
So he be pleased, to think no labour lost.

But at the coming of the King of Heaven
All's set at six and seven;
We wallow in our sin,
Christ cannot find a chamber in the inn.
We entertain him always like a stranger,
And, as at first, still lodge him in the manger.

ANONYMOUS (17th century)

PIED BEAUTY

Glory be to God for dappled things—
   For skies of couple-colour as a brinded cow;
     For rose-moles all in stipple upon trout that swim;
Fresh-firecoal chestnut-falls; finches' wings;
   Landscape plotted and pieced—fold, fallow, and plough;
     And áll trádes, their gear and tackle and trim.
All things counter, original, spare, strange;
   Whatever is fickle, freckled (who knows how?)
     With swift, slow; sweet, sour; adazzle, dim;
He fathers-forth whose beauty is past change:
     Praise him.

GERARD MANLEY HOPKINS (1844–1889)

BALLAD OF THE BREAD MAN

Mary stood in the kitchen
    Baking a loaf of bread.
An angel flew in through the window.
    'We've a job for you,' he said.

'God in his big gold heaven,
    Sitting in his big blue chair,
Wanted a mother for his little son.
    Suddenly saw you there.'

Mary shook and trembled,
    'It isn't true what you say.'
'Don't say that,' said the angel.
    'The baby's on its way.'

Joseph was in the workshop
    Planing a piece of wood.
'The old man's past it,' the neighbours said.
    'That girl's been up to no good.'

'And who was that elegant fellow,'
    They said, 'in the shiny gear?'
The things they said about Gabriel
    Were hardly fit to hear.

Mary never answered,
    Mary never replied.
She kept the information,
    Like the baby, safe inside.

It was election winter.
    They went to vote in town.
When Mary found her time had come
    The hotels let her down.

The baby was born in an annexe
    Next to the local pub.
At midnight, a delegation
    Turned up from the Farmers' Club.

They talked about an explosion
    That made a hole in the sky,
Said they'd been sent to the Lamb and Flag
    To see God come down from on high.

A few days later a bishop
    And a five-star general were seen
With the head of an African country
    In a bullet-proof limousine.

'We've come,' they said, 'with tokens
    For the little boy to choose.'
Told the tale about war and peace
    In the television news.

After them came the soldiers
    With rifle and bomb and gun,
Looking for enemies of the state.
    The family had packed and gone.

When they got back to the village
    The neighbours said, to a man,
'That boy will never be one of us,
    Though he does what he blessed well can.'

He went round to all the people
    A paper crown on his head.
Here is some bread from my father.
    Take, eat, he said.

Nobody seemed very hungry.
    Nobody seemed to care.
Nobody saw the god in himself
    Quietly standing there.

He finished up in the papers.
    He came to a very bad end.
He was charged with bringing the living to life
    No man was that prisoner's friend.

There's only one kind of punishment
    To fit that kind of a crime.
They rigged a trial and shot him dead.
    They were only just in time.

They lifted the young man by the leg,
    They lifted him by the arm,
They locked him in a cathedral
    In case he came to harm.

They stored him safe as water
    Under seven rocks.
One Sunday morning he burst out
    Like a jack-in-the-box.

Through the town he went walking.
    He showed them the holes in his head.
Now do you want any loaves? he cried.
    'Not today,' they said.

CHARLES CAUSLEY

RAPTOR*

You have made God small,
setting him astride
a pipette or a retort
studying the bubbles,
absorbed in an experiment
that will come to nothing.

I think of him rather
as an enormous owl
abroad in the shadows,
brushing me sometimes
with his wing so the blood
in my veins freezes, able

to find his way from one
soul to another because
he can see in the dark.
I have heard him crooning
to himself, so that almost
I could believe in angels,

those feathered overtones
in love's rafters, I have heard
him scream, too, fastening
his talons in his great
adversary, or in some lesser
denizen, maybe, like you or me.

R.S. THOMAS
* robber, esp. bird of prey

I HAVE NOT SEEN GOD

I have not seen God face to face
Therefore I cannot fear Him
But I fear lightning and the anger of righteous men,
And this grasping at space
In a night grown huge behind the trembling stars.

I have not seen God face to face
Therefore I cannot worship Him
But I worship mountains that wear a bloom of grapes
In the evening sun; I worship primitive things—
Trees and essential shapes
Of beauty outlined in the world we touch.

I have not seen God face to face
Therefore I cannot love Him
But I love the light that quickens wood and stone,
The sudden grace
Lifting a dull pedestrian out of time
And place, to find the Unknown through the known.

PHOEBE HESKETH

BE A BUTTERFLY

Don't be a kyatta-pilla
Be a butterfly
old preacher screamed
to illustrate his sermon
of Jesus and the higher life

rivulets of well-earned
sweat sliding down
his muscly mahogany face
in the half-empty school church
we sat shaking with muffling
laughter
watching our mother trying to save
herself from joining the wave

only our father remaining poker face
and afterwards we always
went home to
split peas Sunday soup
with dumplings, fufu and
pigtail

Don't be a kyatta-pilla
Be a butterfly
Be a butterfly

That was de life preacher
and you was right

GRACE NICHOLS

WORKSHOP

Not everyone would describe themselves as religious but religious feeling has been an inspiration for many writers and has given rise to some of the strongest poetry in the language. Whatever our beliefs may or may not be, a reading of their work provides an insight into their thoughts and feelings and may from time to time provide a flash of recognition. Although these poems often reflect specifically Christian concerns, the questions they address are relevant to anyone who thinks about religion from whatever standpoint.

Poems by two priests

(1) George Herbert was a priest in the seventeenth century but he came from a very wealthy and powerful family. He was well known at Court where his brother, Lord Herbert of Cherbury, was a distinguished diplomat. George Herbert was a brilliant scholar. He had a mastery of several languages, a love of music and was appointed university orator at Cambridge. He was highly valued by the king and could easily have been made Secretary of State but he was offered a post as parish priest at Bemerton near Salisbury and his life changed entirely. He chose to dedicate himself to God and to minister to ordinary people. He was greatly loved by his parishioners, particularly the poorer farm labourers whom, it was reported,

> ' . . . did so love and reverence Mr Herbert that they would let their plough rest when Mr Herbert's Saints' Bell rung to Prayers, that they might also offer their devotions to God with him: and would then return back to their plough. And his most holy life was such that it begot such reverence to God, and to him, that they thought themselves the happier, when they carried Mr Herbert's blessing back with them to their labour . . .'

> (from Walton's 'Life' of Herbert, 1670)

Even then Herbert sometimes had to wrestle with a part of himself that was tempted by the kind of public life and the fame he had given up, and his poems often reflect this conflict.

THE PILGRIMAGE

- Hear the poem 'The Pilgrimage' (p. 79) read aloud. Then by yourself:
  — read the poem through again
  — jot down anything you don't quite understand.

In pairs/small groups

- Try to decide what the 'story' of the poem is and write down what seems to happen in each verse as the writer makes his journey.

As a class

- Share your thoughts and discuss:
  — How might the story of the pilgrimage relate to Herbert's own journey through life?
  — What is the effect of the short tailing-off lines at the end of each stanza?
  — How does Herbert make use of the varied line lengths in verse 4 to convey his changing feelings?
  — What do you think is the message of the rather mysterious last verse?

REDEMPTION

- Hear Herbert's sonnet 'Redemption' (p. 79) read aloud.

In pairs

- Try to work out the 'story' of the poem. A poor man who is the tenant of a rich lord goes to him with a suit, or request, to change the terms of his lease ... What happens then? Where does he seek out the Lord? What is he told? Where does he expect to find him on earth? Where does he *actually* find him and with whom? What is his Lord's answer to the tenant's suit or request?

As a group

- The poem is what is known as an *allegory*, a piece of writing where things may not be what they seem on the surface and stand for something else. The story of the poem may suggest another story. What is that other story and what things in the poem remind you of it?
- What do you notice about the images used in the story? On a copy of the poem ring round all the words to do with land and wealth and riches: underline any of the words to do with legal matters and business.
- An allegory usually has a moral meaning. What moral lessons does this poem suggest?
- Now hear the anonymous seventeenth century poem 'Preparations' (p. 80) read aloud. It was written around the same time that Herbert was writing and some people have suggested it might actually be by him. From what you now know of Herbert, what things about it might suggest it could be his?

On your own

- Choose either of these poems by Herbert or the poem 'Preparations' and write an account of how your understanding of what the poem is saying has grown from the time you first heard it read.

(2) Gerard Manley Hopkins was a nineteenth century scholar and Roman Catholic priest whose poems were first published in 1918, 30 years after his death. Many of his poems celebrate his joy and delight in his faith and in what he sees as the wonder and abundance of creation. That powerful emotion is reflected in the skilful and entirely original use of language and rhythm which is his trademark. Listening to or reading Hopkins you will find you need to give yourself to the poem, and trust the poet. If you do, he will carry you with him and won't let you down.

PIED BEAUTY

- Hear 'Pied Beauty' (p. 80) read aloud.

In pairs first, then as a group

— On a copy of the poem, ring round or underline all the alliteration in the poem.
— Count how many sentences there are in the poem.
— Decide what the combined effect of the alliteration and the sentence structure is on the way we read the poem.
— Decide what the poem is saying. Concentrate on the first line and the last two lines.

In groups

- In groups of about five devise a dramatic reading of the poem and, when you are pleased with it, perform it for the class or make a tape recording. You could choose to tackle it as a choral piece with all of you speaking together, or you could split the lines between different readers, or you could mix both techniques. Whatever you do, try not to lose the life and movement of the verse.

COMPARISON

- Read R.S. Thomas's poem 'Raptor' (p. 83) and Phoebe Hesketh's 'I Have Not Seen God' (p. 83).

In pairs

Each writer has a quite different and individual view of what God means to them.

- Talk about the two poems and jot down notes about what God means to each of them.

As a group

R.S. Thomas is himself a priest in Wales.

- Does his image of God surprise you? How do these two ways of thinking about God compare with your own?

'IS LOVE THE ANSWER?'

RIDDLE-ME-REE

My first is in life (not contained within heart)
My second's in whole but never in part.
My third's in forever, but also in vain.
My last's in ending, why not in pain?

is love the answer?

LIZ LOCHHEAD

FIRST LOVE

I ne'er was struck before that hour
    With love so sudden and so sweet.
    Her face it bloomed like a sweet flower
    And stole my heart away complete.
My face turned pale as deadly pale,
    My legs refused to walk away,
And when she looked 'what could I ail?'
    My life and all seemed turned to clay.

And then my blood rushed to my face
    And took my sight away.
The trees and bushes round the place
    Seemed midnight at noonday.
I could not see a single thing,
    Words from my eyes did start;
They spoke as chords do from the string,
    And blood burnt round my heart.

Are flowers the winter's choice?
    Is love's bed always snow?
She seemed to hear my silent voice
    And love's appeal to know.

I never saw so sweet a face
    As that I stood before:
My heart has left its dwelling-place
    And can return no more.

JOHN CLARE (1793–1864)

A RED, RED ROSE

O my luve's like a red, red rose,
    That's newly sprung in June;
O my luve's like the melodie
    That's sweetly played in tune.

As fair art thou, my bonnie lass,
    So deep in luve am I;
And I will luve thee still, my dear,
    Till a' the seas gang dry.

Till a' the seas gang dry, my dear,
    And the rocks melt wi' the sun:
O I will love thee still, my dear,
    While the sands o' life shall run.

And fare thee weel, my only luve,
    And fare thee weel awhile!
And I will come again, my luve,
    Though it were ten thousand mile.

ROBERT BURNS (1759–1796)

HE WISHES FOR THE CLOTHS OF HEAVEN

Had I the heavens' embroidered cloths,
Enwrought with golden and silver light,
The blue and the dim and the dark cloths
Of night and light and the half-light,
I would spread the cloths under your feet:
But I, being poor, have only my dreams;
I have spread my dreams under your feet;
Tread softly because you tread on my dreams.

W.B. YEATS

PLUCKING THE RUSHES

Garden rushes with red shoots,
Long leaves bending to the wind—
You and I in the same boat
Plucking rushes at the Five Lakes.
We started at dawn from the orchid-island;
We rested under the elms till noon.
You and I plucking rushes
Had not plucked a handful when night came!

ANONYMOUS (translator Arthur Waley)

I AM VERY BOTHERED

I am very bothered when I think
of the bad things I have done in my life.
Not least that time in the chemistry lab
when I held a pair of scissors by the blades
and played the handles
in the naked lilac flame of the Bunsen burner;
then called your name, and handed them over.

O the unrivalled stench of branded skin
as you slipped your thumb and middle finger in,
then couldn't shake off the two burning rings. Marked
the doctor said, for eternity.

Don't believe me, please if I say
that was just my butterfingered way, at thirteen,
of asking you if you would marry me.

SIMON ARMITAGE

MEETING AT NIGHT

The grey sea and the long black land;
And the yellow half-moon large and low;
And the startled little waves that leap
In fiery ringlets from their sleep,
As I gain the cove with pushing prow,
And quench its speed i' the slushy sand.

Then a mile of warm sea-scented beach;
Three fields to cross till a farm appears;
A tap at the pane, the quick sharp scratch
And blue spurt of a lighted match,
And a voice less loud, thro' its joys and fears,
Than the two hearts beating each to each!

ROBERT BROWNING (1812–1889)

WHY SO PALE AND WAN?

WHY so pale and wan, fond lover?
        Prithee, why so pale?
Will, when looking well can't move her,
        Looking ill prevail?
        Prithee, why so pale?

Why so dull and mute, young sinner?
        Prithee, why so mute?
Will, when speaking well can't win her,
        Saying nothing do 't?
        Prithee, why so mute?

Quit, quit for shame! This will not move;
        This cannot take her.
If of herself she will not love,
        Nothing can make her:
        The devil take her!

SIR JOHN SUCKLING (1609–1642)

THE PARTING

Since there's no help, come let us kiss and part—
Nay, I have done, you get no more of me;
And I am glad, yea, glad with all my heart,
That thus so cleanly I myself can free.
Shake hands for ever, cancel all our vows,
And when we meet at any time again,
Be it not seen in either of our brows
That we one jot of former love retain.
Now at the last gasp of Love's latest breath,
When, his pulse failing, Passion speechless lies,
When Faith is kneeling by his bed of death,
And Innocence is closing up his eyes,
   —Now if thou wouldst, when all have given him over,
   From death to life thou might'st him yet recover.

MICHAEL DRAYTON (1563–1631)

A WOMAN TO HER LOVER

Do you come to me to bend me to your will
As conqueror to the vanquished
To make of me a bondslave
To bear you children, wearing out my life
In drudgery and silence
No servant will I be
If that be what you ask. O Lover I refuse you!

Or if you think to wed with one from heaven sent
Whose every deed and word and wish is golden
A wingless angel who can do no wrong
Go!—I am no doll to dress and sit for feeble worship
If that be what you ask, fool, I refuse you!

Or if you think in me to find
A creature who will have no greater joy
Than gratify your clamorous desire,
My skin soft only for your fond caresses
My body supple only for your sense delight.
Oh shame, and pity and abasement.
Not for you the hand of any wakened woman of our time.

But Lover, if you ask of me
That I shall be your comrade, friend, and mate,
To live and work, to love and die with you,
That so together we may know the purity and height
Of passion, and of joy and sorrow,
Then O husband, I am yours forever
And our co-equal love will make the stars to laugh with joy
And we shall have the music of the spheres for bridal march
And to its circling fugue pass, hand holding hand
Until we reach the very heart of God.

CHRISTINA WALSH (1870?–1940?)

I WOULDN'T THANK YOU FOR A VALENTINE

(Rap)

I wouldn't thank you for a Valentine
I won't wake up early wondering if the postman's been.
Should 10 red-padded satin hearts arrive with sticky sickly saccharine
Sentiments in very vulgar verses I wouldn't wonder if you meant them.
Two dozen anonymous Interflora roses?
I'd not bother to swither over who sent them!
I wouldn't thank you for a Valentine.

Scrawl SWALK across the envelope
I'd just say 'Same Auld Story
I canny be bothered deciphering it—
I'm up to here with Amore!
The whole Valentine's Day Thing is trivial and commercial,
A cue for unleashing clichés and candyheart motifs to which I personally am not partial.'
Take more than singing Telegrams, or pints of Chanel Five, or sweets,
To get me ordering oysters or ironing my black satin sheets.
I wouldn't thank you for a Valentine.

If you sent me a solitaire and promises solemn,
Took out an ad in the Guardian Personal Column
Saying something very soppy such as 'Who loves ya, Poo?
I'll tell you, I do, Fozzy Bear, that's who!'
You'd entirely fail to charm me, in fact I'd detest it
I wouldn't be eighteen again for anything, I'm glad I'm past it.
I wouldn't thank you for a Valentine.

If you sent me a single orchid, or a pair of Janet Reger's in a heart-shaped box and declared your
    Love Eternal
I'd say I'd not be caught dead in them they were politically suspect and I'd rather something
    thermal.
If you hired a plane and blazed our love in a banner across the skies;
If you bought me something flimsy in a flatteringly wrong size;
If you sent me a postcard with three Xs and told me how you felt
I wouldn't thank you, I'd melt.

LIZ LOCHHEAD

ANANCY'S THOUGHTS ON LOVE

(Anancy is a trickster spider man who appears in many traditional to Caribbean folk tales)

Love got teeth
as old people say
dont know if you walking
on you hand or you feet
but it dont really matter
cause you bound to meet
sooner or later

love is watching hint
big and bold
but refusing to catch it

love is trapping thoughts
in side-eye gaze
long before thoughts see light-of-day

love is sweet mystery
like sleight-of-rain

But love is sweet misery
like taste-of-pain

love is going down winding labyrinth
at loss for words
and loss of head
but Anancy thank God
always have piece of thread
for way back out

or to put it another way
Anancy in love
always save back piece of heart
for peace of mind

JOHN AGARD

FUNERAL BLUES

Stop all the clocks, cut off the telephone.
Prevent the dog from barking with a juicy bone.
Silence the pianos and with muffled drum
Bring out the coffin, let the mourners come.

Let aeroplanes circle moaning overhead
Scribbling on the sky the message He Is Dead,
Put crêpe bows round the white necks of the public doves,
Let the traffic policemen wear black cotton gloves.

He was my North, my South, my East and West,
My working week and my Sunday rest,
My noon, my midnight, my talk, my song:
I thought that love would last for ever: I was wrong.

The stars are not wanted now: put out every one;
Pack up the moon and dismantle the sun:
Pour away the ocean and sweep up the wood,
For nothing now can ever come to any good.

W.H. AUDEN

WORKSHOP

MEETING AND PARTING

Browning's 'Meeting at Night' (p. 88) catches the excitement of a rendezvous between two lovers. One of the ways he builds up the expectation is through describing the journey by boat and on foot and holding back the meeting to the last two lines. Another is through a rhyme scheme that introduces three rhyming sounds in the first half of each verse and repeats them in reverse order in the second half.

Michael Drayton's 'The Parting' (p. 89) is in Shakespearean sonnet form (see Part A, Unit 8). It begins bravely with the acceptance that the two must part – a clean break with no recriminations. But, by the end, the feeling and the thought have changed.

- Discuss the different ways the two poets create the developing emotions of these two situations.

— In Browning's poem, how do the details he chooses help to produce the atmosphere of a lovers' meeting?

— In Drayton's poem, how does the personification (see Part A, Unit 4) of the dying love in the last six lines change the mood?

IDEAL IMAGES

- How much does your image of an ideal boy or girl friend owe to the media, or to the romances of magazines?

— *In pairs*, list all the characteristics that typically go to make up these ideal images. Then make two more corresponding lists of all the *opposite* qualities. From these second lists you should be able to develop two satirical portraits—anti-romantic images which 'send up' the conventional ideas of the ideal boy or girl friend.

UP-DATING

'A Woman to her Lover' (p. 89) is strikingly modern even though it is nearly 100 years old.

- Hear it read aloud, perhaps shared between four different voices. The first three sections are 'female constructs' that the writer fears her lover may have in mind. What phrase best sums up each one? The fourth section is her own 'self-construct' – a 'co-equal love' between man and woman.

- Write a version of this four-part poem using the images, details and ideas of today. You might follow the same framework, beginning the first three sections with, 'If you think . . .' and ending them with 'Love, I refuse you!' – before concluding with your more positive message in a final section.

SONGS

There are a great many songs about love relationships. In a lot of them the music is far more important than the lyrics, but you may know some where the words are effective on their own.

- A group of you could make your own anthology of lyrics on a theme of your choice.

PARENTS AND CHILDREN

YOU BEING BORN

I saw you born.
It was remarkable.
You shot out from between your mother's legs
like a rugby ball from a scrum
and the stocky Geordie midwife caught you neatly
and cried 'Whoops! She's come!'

You had a wrinkled jammy head
and spasmy legs like a portly frog's.
From your belly button a white root waved
that had fed you all the months you'd grown

and ripened in your mother's womb.
And let me tell you – I'm ashamed –
I forgot your mother completely – she had been
those things to me that one day you'll discover
in someone else, and think 'God, this is it!'
– My sweetheart, my warm dream, my red hot lover –

But for those moments, as the doctor
shoved cotton wool up your flat nose
and swabbed your eyes and cleaned your bum
I forgot completely all my life and love
and watched you like a pool of growing light
and whispered to myself 'She's come! She's come!'

BRIAN JONES

POEM FOR A DAUGHTER

'I think I'm going to have it,'
I said, joking between pains.
The midwife rolled competent
sleeves over corpulent milky arms.
'Dear, you never have it,
we deliver it.'
A judgement years proved true.
Certainly I've never had you

as you still have me, Caroline.
Why does a mother need a daughter?
Heart's needle, hostage to fortune,
freedom's end. Yet nothing's more perfect
than that bleating, razor-shaped cry
that delivers a mother to her baby.

The bloodcord snaps that held
their sphere together. The child,
tiny and alone, creates the mother.

A woman's life is her own
until it is taken away
by a first particular cry.
Then she is not alone
but part of the premises
of everything there is:
a time, a tribe, a war.
When we belong to the world
we become what we are.

ANNE STEVENSON

MORNING SONG

Love set you going like a fat gold watch.
The midwife slapped your footsoles, and your bald cry
Took its place among the elements.

Our voices echo, magnifying your arrival. New statue.
In a drafty museum, your nakedness
Shadows our safety. We stand round blankly as walls.

I'm no more your mother
Than the cloud that distils a mirror to reflect its own slow
Effacement at the wind's hand.

All night your moth-breath
Flickers among the flat pink roses. I wake to listen:
A far sea moves in my ear.

One cry, and I stumble from bed, cow-heavy and floral
In my Victorian nightgown.
Your mouth opens clean as a cat's. The window square

Whitens and swallows its dull stars. And now you try
Your handful of notes;
The clear vowels rise like balloons.

SYLVIA PLATH

BY-LOW

By-low, my babe, lie still and sleep;
It grieves me sore to see thee weep.
If thou wert quiet I'd be glad;
Thy mourning makes my sorrow sad.
By-low, my boy, thy mother's joy,
Thy father breeds me great annoy—
    By-low, lie low.

When he began to court my love,
And me with sugared words to move,
His feignings false and flattering cheer
To me that time did not appear.
But now I see most cruelly
He cares not for my babe nor me—
    By-low, lie low.

Lie still, my darling, sleep awhile,
And when thou wak'st thou'lt sweetly smile;
But smile not as thy father did,
To cozen maids—nay, God forbid!
But yet I fear thou wilt grow near
Thy father's heart and face to bear—
    By-low, lie low.

I cannot choose, but ever will
Be loving to thy father still;
Where'er he stay, where'er he ride
My love with him doth still abide.
In weal or woe, where'er he go,
My heart shall not forsake him; so
    By-low, lie low.

ANONYMOUS (about 1400)

TO OUR DAUGHTER

And she is beautiful, our daughter.
Only six months, but a person.
She turns to look at everything, out walking.
All so precious. I mustn't disturb it with words.
People are like great clowns,
Blossom like balloons, black pigeons like eagles,
Water beyond belief.

She holds out her hand to air,
Sea, sky, wind, sun, movement, stillness,
And wants to hold them all.
My finger is her earth connection, me, and earth.

Her head is like an apple, or an egg.
Skin stretched fine over a strong casing,
Her whole being developing from within
And from without: the answer.

And she sings, long notes from the belly or the throat,
Her legs kick her feet up to her nose,
She rests—laid still like a large rose.
She is our child,
The world is not hers, she has to win it.

JENNIFER ARMITAGE

A CHILD HALF-ASLEEP

Stealthily parting the small-hours silence,
a hardly-embodied figment of his brain
comes down to sit with me
as I work late.
Flat-footed, as though his legs and feet
were still asleep.

On a stool,
staring into the fire,
his dummy dangling.

Fire ignites the small coals of his eyes:
it stares back through the holes
into his head, into the darkness.

I ask what woke him.

'A wolf dreamed me,' he says.

TONY CONNOR

FOR HEIDI WITH BLUE HAIR

When you dyed your hair blue
(or, at least, ultramarine
for the clipped sides, with a crest
of jet-black spikes on top)
you were sent home from school

because, as the headmistress put it,
although dyed hair was not
specifically forbidden, yours
was, apart from anything else,
not done in the school colours.

Tears in the kitchen, telephone-calls
to school from your freedom-loving father:
'She's not a punk in her behaviour;
it's just a style.' (You wiped your eyes,
also not in a school colour.)

'She discussed it with me first—
we checked the rules.' 'And anyway, Dad,
it cost twenty-five dollars.
Tell them it won't wash out—not even if I
    wanted to try.'

It would have been unfair to mention
your mother's death, but that
shimmered behind the arguments.
The school had nothing else against you;
the teachers twittered and gave in.

Next day your black friend had hers done
in grey, white and flaxen yellow—
the school colours precisely:
an act of solidarity, a witty
tease. The battle was already won.

FLEUR ADCOCK

I LOVE ME MUDDER (mother)...

I love me mudder and me mudder love me
we come so far from over de sea,
we heard dat de streets were paved with gold
sometime it hot sometime it cold
I love me mudder and me mudder love me
we try fe live in harmony
you might know her as Valerie
but to me she is my mummy.

She shouts at me daddy so loud some time
she don't smoke weed she don't drink wine
she always do the best she can
she work damn hard down ina England,
she's always singing some kind of song
she have big muscles and she very very strong,
she likes pussy cats and she love cashew nuts
she don't bother with no if and buts.

I love me mudder and me mudder love me
we come so far from over de sea
we heard dat de streets were paved with gold
sometime it hot sometime it cold,
I love her and she love me too
and dis is a love I know is true
my family unit extends to you
loving each other is de ting to do.

BENJAMIN ZEPHANIAH

POEM AT THIRTY-NINE

How I miss my father.
I wish he had not been
so tired
when I was
born.

Writing deposit slips and checks
I think of him.
He taught me how.
This is the form,
he must have said:
the way it is done.
I learned to see
bits of paper
as a way
to escape
the life he knew
and even in high school
had a savings
account.

He taught me
that telling the truth
did not always mean
a beating;
though many of my truths
must have grieved him
before the end.

How I miss my father!
He cooked like a person
dancing
in a yoga meditation
and craved the voluptuous
sharing
of good food.

Now I look and cook just like him:
my brain light;
tossing this and that
into the pot;
seasoning none of my life
the same way twice; happy to feed
whoever strays my way.

He would have grown
to admire
the woman I've become:
cooking, writing, chopping wood,
staring into the fire.

ALICE WALKER

WORKSHOP

BIRTH DAYS

The two poems at the start of this section describe, respectively, a father's and a mother's feelings at the birth of a daughter.

- Hear them read aloud and talk about how they are similar and how they differ.
- Write a comparison of the two poems.

MOTHER, FATHER, BABY

Although the exquisite but anonymous poem 'By-Low' on p. 94 is a lullaby about 600 years old, the ideas and the experience behind it are as relevant to us as anything written today.

- Hear the poem read aloud and then in pairs go through it verse by verse and decide what the mother is feeling about her baby boy and his father at each stage. Share your ideas.
- Read the poem 'Morning Song' (p. 94). How does the writer feel about her relationship with her new baby? What words, phrases or images appeal to you and why?
- Now read Jennifer Armitage's poem 'To Our Daughter' (p. 96). How does she see their child and how does she imagine her child sees the world? Is the relationship different from the picture given in 'Morning Song'?

MOTHER, FATHER, CHILD

- The poem 'A Child Half-Asleep' (p. 96) catches a single moment where dream and reality are confused. Or are they? What does the unexpected reversal at the end of the poem suggest?
- 'For Heidi with Blue Hair' (p. 97) tells of an incident when the poet Fleur Adcock's god-daughter, Heidi, went to school with hair dyed blue. Prepare a reading of the poem using three voices – Poet, Father, Heidi – and present it to others in the group. Discuss what happens in the poem and why it happened.
- Benjamin Zephaniah's poem 'I Love Me Mudder' (p. 99) with its strong rhythmic rap bounce demands to be performed. In small groups plan and then perform a reading of the poem. You could simply split it into three sections but it is worth being more adventurous and taking single lines with single voices or saying some of the lines as a group.

PORTRAIT GALLERY

POEM IN OCTOBER

It was my thirtieth year to heaven
Woke to my hearing from harbour and neighbour wood
And the mussel pooled and the heron
Priested shore
The morning beckon
With water praying and call of seagull and rook
And the knock of sailing boats on the net webbed wall
Myself to set foot
That second
In the still sleeping town and set forth.

My birthday began with the water—
Birds and the birds of the winged trees flying my name
Above the farms and the white horses
And I rose
In rainy autumn
And walked abroad in a shower of all my days.
High tide and the heron dived when I took the road
Over the border
And the gates
Of the town closed as the town awoke.

A springful of larks in a rolling
Cloud and the roadside bushes brimming with whistling
Blackbirds and the sun of October
Summery
On the hill's shoulder,
Here were fond climates and sweet singers suddenly
Come in the morning where I wandered and listened
To the rain wringing
Wind blow cold
In the wood faraway under me.

Pale rain over the dwindling harbour
And over the sea wet church the size of a snail
With its horns through mist and the castle
Brown as owls
But all the gardens
Of spring and summer were blooming in the tall tales
Beyond the border and under the lark full cloud.
There would I marvel
My birthday
Away but the weather turned around.

It turned away from the blithe country
And down the other air and the blue altered sky
Streamed again a wonder of summer
With apples
Pears and red currants
And I saw in the turning so clearly a child's
Forgotten mornings when he walked with his mother
Through the parables
Of sun light
And the legends of the green chapels

And the twice told fields of infancy
That his tears burned my cheeks and his heart moved in mine.
These were the woods the river and sea
Where a boy
In the listening
Summertime of the dead whispered the truth of his joy
To the trees and the stones and the fish in the tide.
And the mystery
Sang alive
Still in the water and singingbirds.

And there could I marvel my birthday
Away but the weather turned around. And the true
Joy of the long dead child sang burning
In the sun.
It was my thirtieth
Year to heaven stood there then in the summer noon
Though the town below lay leaved with October blood.
O may my heart's truth
Still be sung
On this high hill in a year's turning.

DYLAN THOMAS

PHENOMENAL WOMAN

Pretty women wonder where my secret lies.
I'm not cute or built to suit a fashion model's size
But when I start to tell them,
They think I'm telling lies.
I say,
It's in the reach of my arms,
The span of my hips,
The stride of my step,
The curl of my lips.
I'm a woman
Phenomenally.
Phenomenal woman,
That's me.

I walk into a room
Just as cool as you please,
And to a man,
The fellows stand or
Fall down on their knees.
Then they swarm around me,
A hive of honey bees.
I say,
It's the fire in my eyes,
And the flash of my teeth,
The swing in my waist,
And the joy in my feet.
I'm a woman
Phenomenally.
Phenomenal woman,
That's me.

Men themselves have wondered
What they see in me.
They try so much
But they can't touch
My inner mystery.
When I try to show them
They say they still can't see.
I say,
It's in the arch of my back,
The sun of my smile,
The ride of my breasts,
The grace of my style.
I'm a woman
Phenomenally.
Phenomenal woman,
That's me.

Now you understand
Just why my head's not bowed.
I don't shout or jump about

Or have to talk real loud.
When you see me passing
It ought to make you proud.
I say,
It's in the click of my heels,
The bend of my hair,
The palm of my hand,
The need for my care.
'Cause I'm a woman
Phenomenally.
Phenomenal woman,
That's me.

MAYA ANGELOU

THE FAT BLACK WOMAN GOES SHOPPING

Shopping in London winter
is a real drag for the fat black woman
going from store to store
in search of accommodating clothes
and de weather so cold

Look at the frozen thin mannequins
fixing her with grin
and de pretty face salesgals
exchanging slimming glances
thinking she don't notice

Lord is aggravating

Nothing soft and bright and billowing
to flow like breezy sunlight
when she walking

The fat black woman curses in Swahili/Yoruba
and nation language under her breathing
all this journeying and journeying

The fat black woman could only conclude
that when it comes to fashion
the choice is lean

      Nothing much beyond size 14

GRACE NICHOLS

LISTN BIG BRODDA DREAD, NA!

My sista is younga dan mi.
My sista outsmart five-foot three.
My sista is own car repairer
and yu nah catch me doin judo with her.

> I sey I wohn get a complex.
> I wohn get a complex.
> Den I see de muscles my sista flex.

My sista is tops at disco dance.
My sista is well into self-reliance.
My sista plays guitar and drums
and wahn si her knock back double rums.

> I sey I wohn get a complex.
> I wohn get a complex.
> Den I see de muscles my sista flex.

My sista doesn mind smears of grease and dirt.
My sista'll reduce you with sheer muscle hurt.
My sista says no guy goin keep her phone-bound—
wid own car mi sista is a wheel-hound.

> I sey I wohn get a complex.
> I wohn get a complex.
> Den I see de muscles my sista flex.

JAMES BERRY

WARNING

When I am an old woman I shall wear purple
With a red hat which doesn't go, and doesn't suit me.
And I shall spend my pension on brandy and summer gloves
And satin sandals, and say we've no money for butter.
And I shall sit down on the pavement when I'm tired
And gobble up samples in shops and press alarm bells
And run my stick along the public railings
And make up for the sobriety of my youth.
I shall go out in my slippers in the rain
And pick the flowers in other people's gardens
And learn to spit.

You can wear terrible shirts and grow more fat
And eat three pounds of sausages at a go
Or only bread and pickle for a week
And hoard pens and pencils and beermats and things in boxes.

But now we must have clothes that keep us dry
And pay our rent and not swear in the street
And set a good example for the children.
We must have friends to dinner and read the papers.

But maybe I ought to practise a little now?
So people who know me are not too shocked and surprised
When suddenly I am old, and start to wear purple.

JENNY JOSEPH

MY GRANDMOTHER

She kept an antique shop—or it kept her.
Among Apostle spoons and Bristol glass,
The faded silks, the heavy furniture,
She watched her own reflection in the brass
Salvers and silver bowls, as if to prove
Polish was all, there was no need of love.

And I remember how I once refused
To go out with her, since I was afraid.
It was perhaps a wish not to be used
Like antique objects. Though she never said
That she was hurt, I still could feel the guilt
Of that refusal, guessing how she felt.

Later, too frail to keep a shop, she put
All her best things in one long narrow room.
The place smelt old, of things too long kept shut,
The smell of absences where shadows come
That can't be polished. There was nothing then
To give her own reflection back again.

And when she died I felt no grief at all,
Only the guilt of what I once refused.
I walked into her room among the tall
Sideboards and cupboards—things she never used
But needed: and no finger-marks were there,
Only the new dust falling through the air.

ELIZABETH JENNINGS

THE HUNCHBACK IN THE PARK

The hunchback in the park
A solitary mister
Propped between trees and water
From the opening of the garden lock
That lets the trees and water enter
Until the Sunday sombre bell at dark

Eating bread from a newspaper
Drinking water from the chained cup
That the children filled with gravel
In the fountain basin where I sailed my ship
Slept at night in a dog kennel
But nobody chained him up.

Like the park birds he came early
Like the water he sat down
And Mister they called Hey mister
The truant boys from the town
Running when he had heard them clearly
On out of sound

Past lake and rockery
Laughing when he shook his paper
Hunchbacked in mockery
Through the loud zoo of the willow groves
Dodging the park keeper
With his stick that picked up leaves.

And the old dog sleeper
Alone between nurses and swans
While the boys among willows
Made the tigers jump out of their eyes
To roar on the rockery stones
And the groves were blue with sailors

Made all day until bell time
A woman figure without fault
Straight as a young elm
Straight and tall from his crooked bones
That she might stand in the night
After the locks and chains

All night in the unmade park
After the railings and shrubberies
The birds the grass the trees the lake
And the wild boys innocent as strawberries
Had followed the hunchback
To his kennel in the dark.

DYLAN THOMAS

THE HIPPOPOTAMUSMAN

Into the world of the red glass bus
came a man with a face like a
hippopotamus

Grotesqueeruptions made horrific
an otherwise normal ugly face
Wartsscrambled over his head
peeping between thin twigs of dry hair
like pink shiny sunsets
Hanging below the neckline
like grapes festering on a vine
And when he blinked
you could glimpse the drunken dance
in the whites of his eyes
like the flash of underpants
through unbuttoned trouserflies

Had the passengers been in groups
there might have been laughter
But they were all singles
and turning their faces to the windows
did not see the view
but behind the privacy of eyelids
had a mental spew

Limpinggropingly looking for a place
went the substandard man
with the hunchbacked face
and finding one sat
and beholding his mudstudded boots
the hippopotamusman
wondered whether it was wednesday.

ROGER McGOUGH

TEN TYPES OF HOSPITAL VISITOR

I

The first enters wearing the neon armour
Of virtue.
Ceaselessly firing all-purpose smiles
At everyone present
She destroys hope
In the breasts of the sick,
Who realize instantly
That they are incapable of surmounting
Her ferocious goodwill.

Such courage she displays
In the face of human disaster!

Fortunately, she does not stay long.
After a speedy trip round the ward
In the manner of a nineteen-thirties destroyer
Showing the flag in the Mediterranean,
She returns home for a week
—With luck, longer—
Scorched by the heat of her own worthiness.

II

The second appears, a melancholy splurge
Of theological colours;
Taps heavily about like a healthy vulture
Distributing deep-frozen hope.

The patients gaze at him cautiously.
Most of them, as yet uncertain of the realities
Of heaven, hell-fire, or eternal emptiness,
Play for safety
By accepting his attentions
With just-concealed apathy,
Except one old man, who cries
With newly sharpened hatred,
'Shove off! Shove off!
'Shove ... shove ... shove ... shove
Off!
Just you
Shove!'

III

The third skilfully deflates his weakly smiling victim
By telling him
How the lobelias are doing,
How many kittens the cat had,
How the slate came off the scullery roof,
And how no one has visited the patient for a fortnight
Because everybody
Had colds and feared to bring the jumpy germ
Into hospital.

The patient's eyes
Ice over. He is uninterested
In lobelias, the cat, the slate, the germ.
Flat on his back, drip-fed, his face
The shade of a newly dug-up Pharaoh,
Wearing his skeleton outside his skin,
Yet his wits as bright as a lighted candle,
He is concerned only with the here, the now,
And requires to speak
Of nothing but his present predicament.

It is not permitted.

IV

The fourth attempts to cheer
His aged mother with light jokes
Menacing as shell-splinters.
'They'll soon have you jumping round
Like a gazelle,' he says.
'Playing in the football team.'
Quite undeterred by the sight of kilos
Of plaster, chains, lifting-gear,
A pair of lethally designed crutches,
'You'll be leap-frogging soon,' he says.
'Swimming ten lengths of the baths.'

At these unlikely prophecies
The old lady stares fearfully
At her sick, sick offspring
Thinking he has lost his reason—

Which, alas, seems to be the case.

V

The fifth, a giant from the fields
With suit smelling of milk and hay,
Shifts uneasily from one bullock foot
To the other, as though to avoid
Settling permanently in the antiseptic landscape.
Occasionally he looses a scared glance
Sideways, as though fearful of what intimacy
He may blunder on, or that the walls
Might suddenly close in on him.

He carries flowers, held lightly in fingers
The size and shape of plantains,
Tenderly kisses his wife's cheek
—The brush of a child's lips—
Then balances, motionless, for thirty minutes
On the thin chair.

At the end of visiting time
He emerges breathless,
Blinking with relief, into the safe light.

He does not appear to notice
The dusk.

VI

The sixth visitor says little,
Breathes reassurance,
Smiles securely.
Carries no black passport of grapes
And visa of chocolate. Has a clutch
Of clean washing.

Unobtrusively stows it
In the locker; searches out more.
Talks quietly to the Sister
Out of sight, out of earshot, of the patient.
Arrives punctually as a tide.
Does not stay the whole hour.

Even when she has gone
The patient seems to sense her there:
An upholding
Presence.

VII

The seventh visitor
Smells of bar-room after-shave.
Often finds his friend
Sound asleep: whether real or feigned
Is never determined.

He does not mind; prowls the ward
In search of second-class, lost-face patients
With no visitors
And who are pretending to doze
Or read paperbacks.

He probes relentlessly the nature
Of each complaint, and is swift with such
Dilutions of confidence as,
'Ah! You'll be worse
Before you're better.'

Five minutes before the bell punctuates
Visiting time, his friend opens an alarm-clock eye.
The visitor checks his watch.
Market day. The Duck and Pheasant will be still open.

Courage must be refuelled.

VIII

The eighth visitor looks infinitely
More decayed, ill and infirm than any patient.
His face is an expensive grey.

He peers about with antediluvian eyes
As though from the other end
Of time.
He appears to have risen from the grave
To make this appearance.
There is a whiff of white flowers about him;
The crumpled look of a slightly used shroud.
Slowly he passes the patient
A bag of bullet-proof
Home-made biscuits,
A strong, death-dealing cake—
'To have with your tea,'
Or a bowl of fruit so weighty
It threatens to break
His glass fingers.

The patient, encouraged beyond measure,
Thanks him with enthusiasm, not for
The oranges, the biscuits, the cake,
But for the healing sight
Of someone patently worse
Than himself. He rounds the crisis-corner;
Begins a recovery.

IX

The ninth visitor is life.

X

The tenth visitor
Is not usually named.

CHARLES CAUSLEY

WORKSHOP

SELF-PORTRAITS

'Poem in October' (p. 102) and 'Phenomenal Woman' (p. 104) are both celebratory poems, written in the first person.

● Hear them read aloud and talk about the feelings they express. You could try your own birthday poem, or write 'Phenomenal Man'.

WRITING BACK

Two solitary men are the subjects of the poems on p. 108. Dylan Thomas pictures the lonely hunchback teased by local boys; Roger McGough describes a man with a severely disfigured face and the effect he has on the bus passengers.

But what if these men wrote back to these writers, challenging, explaining, maybe resenting their portraits?

● Choose *one* of these poems, re-read it and try to think yourself into the role of the man described. Jot down some notes about the people and places you see from *your* point of view and record your thoughts and feelings. You may realise that you are being watched. Write back to the poet.

Role play

By treating Charles Causley's poem, 'Ten Types of Hospital Visitor' (pp. 109–112), as a script to be performed you can gain a sense of the sharply different characters he gives us.

● One way to tackle the poem is to divide the class into two large groups with between 12 and 15 per group, allowing for ten 'visitors' and several 'patients'. Each half of the class then works on a dramatised reading of the poem to be presented to the others. In two groups:
— decide who will portray the 'visitors' and the 'patients'
— how will the text be heard? By a single narrator, or by several voices?
— look carefully at the details of movement, age, manner, and speech given in the sections. How will you portray each visitor?
— how will you dramatise numbers 9 and 10?

● Rehearse your dramatised reading and present it to the rest of the class.

WORK

SONG OF THE WAGONDRIVER

My first love was the ten-ton truck
they gave me when I started,
and though she played the bitch with me
I grieved when we were parted.

Since then I've had a dozen more,
the wound was quick to heal,
and now it's easier to say
I'm married to my wheel.

I've trunked it north, I've trunked it south,
on wagons good and bad,
but none were ever really like
the first I ever had.

The life is hard, the hours are long,
sometimes I cease to feel,
but I go on, for it seems to me
I'm married to my wheel.

Often I think of my home and kids,
out on the road at night,
and think of taking a local job
provided the money's right.

Two nights a week I see my wife,
and eat a decent meal,
but otherwise, for all my life,
I'm married to my wheel.

B.S. JOHNSON

TOADS

Why should I let the toad *work*
    Squat on my life?
Can't I use my wit as a pitchfork
    And drive the brute off?

Six days of the week it soils
    With its sickening poison—
Just for paying a few bills!
    That's out of proportion.

Lots of folk live on their wits:
    Lecturers, lispers,
Losels[1], loblolly-men[2], louts—
    They don't end as paupers;

Lots of folk live up lanes
    With fires in a bucket,
Eat windfalls and tinned sardines—
    They seem to like it.

Their nippers have got bare feet,
    Their unspeakable wives
Are skinny as whippets—and yet
    No one actually *starves*.

Ah, were I courageous enough
    To shout, *Stuff your pension!*
But I know, all too well, that's the stuff
    That dreams are made on:

For something sufficiently toad-like
    Squats in me too;
Its hunkers are heavy as hard luck,
    And cold as snow,

And will never allow me to blarney
    My way to getting
The fame and the girl and the money
    All at one sitting.

I don't say, one bodies the other
    One's spiritual truth;
But I do say it's hard to lose either,
    When you have both.

PHILIP LARKIN

[1] Good-for-nothings
[2] Country Bumpkins

STRIPPING WALLS

I have been practical as paint today, wholesome as bread—
I have stripped walls. I rose early and felt clean-limbed
And steady-eyed and said 'Today I will strip those walls.'
I have not been chewing my nails and gazing through windows
And grovelling for a subject or happiness. There was the subject.
Simple and tall. And when the baker called he was civil
And looking at me with some respect he said
'I see you're stripping walls'—I could see he liked me.
And when I opened the door to the greengrocer, I glinted my eyes
And leaned nonchalantly and poked some tomatoes and said as an aside
'I'm stripping walls today,' 'Are you?' he asked, interested, and I said
'Yes, just stripping those walls.' I could feel my forearms thicken, grow
Hairy, and when the laundry arrived I met it with rolled sleeves.
'Stripping walls?' he asked. 'Yeah,' I said, as if it were unimportant,
'Stripping walls. You know.' He nodded and smiled as if he knew.
And with a step like a spring before the meal I strode
Down to the pub and leaned and sipped ale and heard them talk
How one had cleared land that morning, another chopped wood.
When an eye caught mine I winked and flipped my head. 'I've been
Stripping walls,' I said. 'Have you?' 'Yeah, you know, just stripping.'
They nodded. 'Can be tricky,' one mumbled. I nodded. 'It can be that.'
'Plaster,' another said. 'Holes,' I said. 'Workmanship,' said another
And shook his head. 'Yeah, have a drink,' I said.
And whistled through the afternoon, and stood once or twice
At the door-jamb, the stripper dangling from my fingers.
'Stripping?' asked passing neighbours. I nodded and they went on happy—
They were happy that I was stripping walls. It meant a lot.
When it grew dark, I went out for the freshness, 'Hey!' I called up,
'I've been stripping walls!' 'Just fancy that!' answered the moon with
A long pale face like Hopkins. 'Hey fellers!' he called to the stars,
'This little hairy runt has been stripping walls!' 'Bully for him,' chimed
The Pole star, remote and cool as Virgil, 'He's a good, good lad.'
I crept to the kitchen, pursued by celestial laughter
'You've done well today,' she said. 'Shall we paint tomorrow?'
'Ah, shut up!' I said, and started hacking my nails.

BRIAN JONES

WORK

There is no point in work
unless it absorbs you
like an absorbing game.

If it doesn't absorb you
if it's never any fun,
don't do it.

When a man goes out into his work
he is alive like a tree in spring,
he is living, not merely working.

D.H. LAWRENCE

WOMAN WORK

I've got the children to tend
The clothes to mend.
The floor to mop
The food to shop
Then the chicken to fry
The baby to dry
I got company to feed
The garden to weed
I've got the shirts to press
The tots to dress
The cane to be cut
I gotta clean up this hut
Then see about the sick
And the cotton to pick.

Shine on me, sunshine
Rain on me, rain
Fall softly, dewdrops
And cool my brow again.

Storm, blow me from here
With your fiercest wind
Let me float across the sky
'Til I can rest again.

Fall gently, snowflakes
Cover me with white
Cold icy kisses and
Let me rest tonight.

Sun, rain, curving sky
Mountain, oceans, leaf and stone
Star shine, moon glow
You're all that I can call my own.

MAYA ANGELOU

TOADS REVISITED

Walking around in the park
Should feel better than work:
The lake, the sunshine,
The grass to lie on,

Blurred playground noises
Beyond black-stockinged nurses—
Not a bad place to be
Yet it doesn't suit me,

Being one of the men
You meet of an afternoon:
Palsied old step-takers,
Hare-eyed clerks with the jitters,

Waxed-fleshed out-patients
Still vague from accidents,
And characters in long coats
Deep in the litter-baskets—

All dodging the toad work
By being stupid or weak.
Think of being them!
Hearing the hours chime,

Watching the bread delivered,
The sun by clouds covered,
The children going home;
Think of being them,

Turning over their failures
By some bed of lobelias,
Nowhere to go but indoors,
No friends but empty chairs—

No, give me my in-tray,
My loaf-haired secretary,
My shall-I-keep-the-call-in-Sir:
What else can I answer,

When the lights come on at four
At the end of another year?
Give me your arm, old toad;
Help me down Cemetery Road.

PHILIP LARKIN

WATERPOT

The daily going out
and coming in
always being hurried
along
like like . . . cattle

In the evenings
returning from the fields
she tried hard to walk
like a woman

she tried very hard
pulling herself erect
with every three or four
steps
pulling herself together
holding herself like
royal cane

And the overseer
hurrying them along
in the quickening darkness

And the overseer sneering
them along in the quickening
darkness
sneered at the pathetic
the pathetic display
of dignity

O but look
there's a waterpot growing
from her head

GRACE NICHOLS

WORKSHOP

PERFORMANCES

In groups take up one of the following suggestions for producing a reading or
performance of one of the poems in this section. Aim to put all your different
performances together into one seamless radio programme or performance on the
theme of Work. You may want to write some linking pieces or to add poems of your
own.

- 'Song of the Wagondriver' (p. 114) is a modern work song and is written as a ballad.
  — In small groups discuss how the writer sees his relationship with his truck, write
  down key phrases and then share your ideas.
  — There are a number of ways in which the poem could be spoken or sung but it
  suggests the country and western style. In small groups you could either rehearse

and perform a reading using several voices or a musical version with guitar accompaniment.

- 'Work' (p. 116) is a short poem by D.H. Lawrence that can be read by three voices each taking a verse. Try to read it in such a way that Lawrence's strong feelings come across.

- 'Stripping Walls' (p. 115) is best spoken in the satisfied voice of someone who feels pleased about his DIY work. It is interspersed with odd bits of dialogue from the baker, the greengrocer, the laundry man, the men in the pub, the neighbours, the moon, the Pole star and the poet's wife.
  — Hear the poem read aloud and talk about what it is that gives the writer so much pleasure about his hard physical work. When he is not flexing his muscles, Brian Jones is an English teacher.

- 'Woman Work' (p. 117) begins with a busy, bustling list of all the chores to be done, then it changes to four slower, more gentle verses. Perhaps a group of about four girls could create the breathless movement of the first lines by 'overlaying' one line with the next, using several voices. Then the four more reflective verses could each be read by single voices.

TOADS/TOADS REVISITED

- Hear Philip Larkin's poem 'Toads' (p. 114) read aloud. In groups, decide what he is complaining about. What does he think he wants? What stops him from going for it? What kind of person comes across to you?

- Now hear his later poem 'Toads Revisited' (p. 118). In groups, decide what might be the attractions of being like the people in the park. What puts the writer off the thought of joining them? What, in the end, are the attractions of his job? Where does it all end, anyway? What kind of person comes across to you?
  — How are the views he expresses in the two poems similar and how are they different?

- Read D.H. Lawrence's short poem 'Work' on p. 116. Discuss how you imagine he would have viewed Larkin's attitude to work.

- Write a comment about Larkin's poems showing how far you sympathise with and how far you disagree with his views.

WORK NOW

- In pairs/small groups, talk about the types of non-school work you do at present or have done in the past. Some of you may do household chores to earn extra cash – washing up, shopping, helping in the garden, cleaning the car for example – or you may do all you can to avoid them. You may have hobbies which involve you in work – such as bike or kit maintenance, preparing tackle, keeping fit. Or you may have a paid part-time job – working on a delivery round, or in a shop. Talk about what you most enjoy and what you dislike about such work and why you feel as you do.

- On your own write, a piece which catches both the problems and the pleasures of such work. You might find the opening of Maya Angelou's poem on p. 117 gives you a model you could use. Think of all the little demands that the work makes and list them as she does.

CREATURES

ESTHER'S TOMCAT

Daylong this tomcat lies stretched flat
As an old rough mat, no mouth and no eyes.
Continual wars and wives are what
Have tattered his ears and battered his head.

Like a bundle of old rope and iron
Sleeps till blue dusk. Then reappear
His eyes, green as ringstones: he yawns wide red,
Fangs fine as a lady's needle and bright.

A tomcat sprang at a mounted knight,
Locked round his neck like a trap of hooks
While the knight rode fighting its clawing and bite.
After hundreds of years the stain's there

On the stone where he fell, dead of the tom:
That was at Barnborough. The tomcat still
Grallochs★ odd dogs on the quiet,
Will take the head clean off your simple pullet,

Is unkillable. From the dog's fury,
From gunshot fired point-blank he brings
His skin whole, and whole
From owlish moons of bekittenings

Among ashcans. He leaps and lightly
Walks upon sleep, his mind on the moon
Nightly over the round world of men,
Over the roofs go his eyes and outcry.

TED HUGHES

★ disembowels

CAT

cold white cat
waiting
in the lamplight
floodlit
in the dark night
always watching
always waiting
green-eyed and strange
for my return.
the distance
between us
is infinite
you content
in the immediacy
of the cold night
me seeking security
behind a darkened door.
you never purr
or move towards me
to rub against my ankles
but watch and wait
whilst I hurry down the street
fumble for my key
and enter the house.
I shut you out
but you're always there
each morning
each evening
the consciousness
within
my sleep.

SUE KELLY

FROGS

Frogs sit more solid
Than anything sits. In mid-leap they are
Parachutists falling
In a free fall. They die on roads
With arms across their chests and
Heads high.

I love frogs that sit
Like Buddha, that fall without
Parachutes, that die
Like Italian tenors.

Above all, I love them because,
Pursued in water, they never
Panic so much that they fail
To make stylish triangles
With their ballet dancer's
Legs.

NORMAN MacCAIG

THE KITTEN AND FALLING LEAVES

See the kitten on the wall
Sporting with the leaves that fall,
Withered leaves—one—two—and three—
From the lofty elder tree!

—But the kitten, how she starts,
Crouches, stretches, paws, and darts!
First at one, and then its fellow
Just as light and just as yellow;
There are many now—now one—
Now they stop and there are none.
What intenseness of desire
In her upward eye of fire!
With a tiger-leap half way
Now she meets the coming prey,
Lets it go as fast, and then
Has it in her power again:
Now she works with three or four,
Like an Indian conjurer,
Quick as he in feats of art,
Far beyond in joy of heart . . .

WILLIAM WORDSWORTH (1770–1850)

HAWK ROOSTING

I sit in the top of the wood, my eyes closed.
Inaction, no falsifying dream
Between my hooked head and hooked feet:
Or in sleep rehearse perfect kills and eat.

The convenience of the high trees!
The air's buoyancy and the sun's ray
Are of advantage to me;
And the earth's face upward for my inspection.

My feet are locked upon the rough bark.
It took the whole of Creation
To produce my foot, my each feather:
Now I hold Creation in my foot

Or fly up, and revolve it all slowly—
I kill where I please because it is all mine.
There is no sophistry in my body:
My manners are tearing off heads—

The allotment of death.
For the one path of my flight is direct
Through the bones of the living.
No arguments assert my right:

The sun is behind me.
Nothing has changed since I began.
My eye has permitted no change.
I am going to keep things like this.

TED HUGHES

THE STAG

While the rain fell on the November woodland shoulder of Exmoor
While the traffic jam along the road honked and shouted
Because the farmers were parking wherever they could
And scrambling to the bank-top to stare through the tree-fringe
Which was leafless,
The stag ran through his private forest.

While the rain drummed on the roofs of the parked cars
And the kids inside cried and daubed their chocolate and fought
And mothers and aunts and grandmothers
Were a tangle of undoing sandwiches and screwed-round gossiping heads
Steaming up the windows,
The stag loped through his favourite valley.

While the blue horsemen down in the boggy meadow
Sodden nearly black, on sodden horses,
Spaced as at a military parade,
Moved a few paces to the right and a few to the left and felt rather foolish
Looking at the brown impassable river,
The stag came over the last hill of Exmoor.

While everybody high-kneed it to the bank-top all along the road
Where steady men in oilskins were stationed at binoculars,
And the horsemen by the river galloped anxiously this way and that
And the cry of hounds came tumbling invisibly with their echoes down through the draggle of trees,
Swinging across the wall of dark woodland,
The stag dropped into a strange country.

And turned at the river
Hearing the hound-pack smash the undergrowth, hearing the bell-note
Of the voice that carried all the others,
Then while his limbs all cried different directions to his lungs, which only wanted to rest,
The blue horsemen on the bank opposite
Pulled aside the camouflage of their terrible planet.

And the stag doubled back weeping and looking for home up a valley and down a valley
While the strange trees struck at him and the brambles lashed him,
And the strange earth came galloping after him carrying the loll-tongued hounds to fling all over him
And his heart became just a club beating his ribs and his own hooves shouted with hounds' voices,
And the crowd on the road got back into their cars
Wet-through and disappointed.

TED HUGHES

SNAKE

A snake came to my water-trough
On a hot, hot day, and I in pyjamas for the heat,
To drink there.

In the deep, strange-scented shade of the great dark carob-tree
I came down the steps with my pitcher
And must wait, must stand and wait, for there he was at the trough before me.

He reached down from a fissure in the earth-wall in the gloom
And trailed his yellow-brown slackness soft-bellied down, over the edge of the stone trough
And rested his throat upon the stone bottom,
And where the water had dripped from the tap, in a small clearness,
He sipped with his straight mouth,
Softly drank through his straight gums, into his slack long body,
Silently.

Someone was before me at my water-trough,
And I, like a second comer, waiting.

He lifted his head from his drinking, as cattle do,
And looked at me vaguely, as drinking cattle do,
And flickered his two-forked tongue from his lips, and mused a moment,
And stooped and drank a little more,
Being earth-brown, earth-golden from the burning bowels of the earth
On the day of Sicilian July, with Etna smoking.

The voice of my education said to me
He must be killed,
For in Sicily the black, black snakes are innocent, the gold are venomous.
And voices in me said, If you were a man
You would take a stick and break him now, and finish him off.

But must I confess how I liked him,
How glad I was that he had come like a guest in quiet, to drink at my water-trough
And depart peaceful, pacified and thankless,
Into the burning bowels of this earth?

Was it cowardice, that I dared not kill him?
Was it perversity, that I longed to talk to him?
Was it humility, to feel so honoured?
I felt so honoured.

And yet those voices:
If you were not afraid, you would kill him!

And truly I was afraid, I was most afraid,
But even so, honoured still more
That he should seek my hospitality
From out the dark door of the secret earth.

He drank enough
And lifted his head, dreamily, as one who has drunken,
And flickered his tongue like a forked night on the air, so black;
Seeming to lick his lips,
And looked around like a god, unseeing, into the air,
And slowly turned his head,
And slowly, very slowly, as if thrice adream,
Proceeded to draw his slow length curving round
And climb again the broken bank of my wall-face.

And as he put his head into that dreadful hole,
And as he slowly drew up, snake-easing his shoulders, and entered farther,
A sort of horror, a sort of protest against his withdrawing into that horrid black hole,
Deliberately going into the blackness, and slowly drawing himself after,
Overcame me now his back was turned.

I looked round, I put down my pitcher,
I picked up a clumsy log
And threw it at the water-trough with a clatter.

I think it did not hit him,
But suddenly that part of him that was left behind convulsed in undignified haste,
Writhed like lightning, and was gone
Into the black hole, the earth-lipped fissure in the wall-front,
At which, in the intense still noon, I stared with fascination.

And immediately I regretted it.
I thought how paltry, how vulgar, what a mean act!
I despised myself and the voices of my accursed human education.

And I thought of the albatross,
And I wished he would come back, my snake.
For he seemed to me again like a king,
Like a king in exile, uncrowned in the underworld,
Now due to be crowned again.

And so, I missed my chance with one of the lords
Of life.
And I have something to expiate;
A pettiness.

D.H. LAWRENCE

THE DALLIANCE OF THE EAGLES

Skirting the river road, (my forenoon walk, my rest,)
Skyward in air a sudden muffled sound, the dalliance of the eagles,
The rushing amorous contact high in space together,
The clinching interlocking claws, a living, fierce, gyrating wheel,
Four beating wings, two beaks, a swirling mass tight grappling,
In tumbling turning clustered loops, straight downward falling,
Till o'er the river pois'd, the twain yet one, a moment's lull,
A motionless still balance in the air, then parting, talons loosing,
Upward again on slow-firm pinions slanting, their separate diverse flight,
She hers, he his, pursuing.

WALT WHITMAN (1819–1892)

THE WILD SWANS AT COOLE

The trees are in their autumn beauty,
The woodland paths are dry,
Under the October twilight the water
Mirrors a still sky;
Upon the brimming water among the stones
Are nine-and-fifty swans.

The nineteenth autumn has come upon me
Since I first made my count;
I saw, before I had well finished,
All suddenly mount
And scatter wheeling in great broken rings
Upon their clamorous wings.

I have looked upon those brilliant creatures,
And now my heart is sore.
All's changed since I, hearing at twilight,
The first time on this shore,
The bell-beat of their wings above my head,
Trod with a lighter tread.

Unwearied still, lover by lover,
They paddle in the cold
Companionable streams or climb the air;
Their hearts have not grown old;
Passion or conquest, wander where they will,
Attend upon them still.

But now they drift upon the still water,
Mysterious, beautiful;
Among what rushes will they build,
By what lake's edge or pool
Delight men's eyes when I awake some day
To find they have flown away?

W.B. YEATS

TROUT

Hangs, a fat gun-barrel,
deep under arched bridges
or slips like butter down
the throat of the river.

From depths smooth-skinned as plums
his muzzle gets bull's eye;
picks off grass-seed and moths
that vanish, torpedoed.

Where water unravels
over gravel-beds he
is fired from the shallows
white belly reporting

flat; darts like a tracer-
bullet back between stones
and is never burnt out.
A volley of cold blood

ramrodding the current.

SEAMUS HEANEY

WORKSHOP

CAPTURING POETS

We quoted Ted Hughes' 'Capturing Animals' (Part A, Unit 1) because it illustrated
the living quality of words in poems; this is nowhere more apparent than in the
animal poetry of Hughes himself and of an earlier writer who was also a skilled
creator of creatures in words – D.H. Lawrence. Both are represented in this section,
Hughes with three poems (pp. 121, 124 and 125), Lawrence with one of his longer
pieces, 'Snake' (p. 126). Find other animal poems by these writers. (Look at Ted
Hughes' *New Selected Poems, 1957–94* and *Under the North Star*, Faber; and D.H.
Lawrence's *Selected Poems*, Penguin.)

In groups

- Select several animal poems that you like by Hughes and Lawrence and devise a short
radio programme which captures the style of either or both of the writers and
introduces their poetry to a young audience. Script a suitable introduction and linking
passages, rehearse your readings, and record your programme on cassette tape.

On your own

- Write your own animal poem in the style of Lawrence or Hughes. Perhaps you can
invent a verse that each might write about the same creature.

ENCOUNTER
In groups

- Hear 'Snake' read aloud. It's probably best shared between two voices, section by section.

- Talk about the main ideas of the poem and note down the places where Lawrence's thoughts and feelings change. You could present these as a flow-diagram; or as a graph with different coloured lines for 'the voices of his education' and for his instinctive feelings of admiration for the snake. Either way, show how the narrative of the poem develops.

On your own

- Try writing an anecdote of your own, real or imagined, about a creature. First, plot out *the events, in sequence*, concentrating simply on what happened. Then, plot out *the internal narrative* of your own changing thoughts and feelings. Work the two in together to make your own poem.

CLASS BESTIARY

Most of the creatures in this section are caught in particular images:
— a tomcat . . . 'lies stretched flat / As an old rough mat'
— frogs . . . 'sit / Like Buddha'
— swans . . . 'scatter wheeling in great broken rings'
— eagles . . . 'clinching, interlocking claws'
— a trout . . . 'a fat gun–barrel'

- Make up your own class bestiary. All you need to start is a sheet of paper and a different animal for everyone in the class, though pictures of animals would help.
  — Head up each sheet with the animal's name (and picture if you have one).
  — Write *one* short 'image association', like those above, and pass your paper on. Circulate the papers until you have collected as many images as possible.
  — Work the ideas and images the class has given you into a list-poem or prose description of the animal. The class bestiary can then be put up for display.

POEMS TO COMPARE

(a)

DELIGHT IN DISORDER

A sweet disorder in the dresse
Kindles in cloathes a wantonnesse:
A Lawne about the shoulders thrown
Into a fine distraction:
An erring Lace, which here and there
Enthralls the Crimson Stomacher:
A Cuffe neglectfull and thereby
Ribbands to flow confusedly:
A winning wave (deserving Note)
In the tempestuous petticote:
A carelesse shooe-string, in whose tye
I see a wilde civility:
Doe more bewitch me, than when Art
Is too precise in every part.

ROBERT HERRICK (1591–1674)

SWEET NEGLECT

Still to be neat, still to be drest,
As you were going to a feast:
Still to be powdered, still perfumed:
Lady, it is to be presumed.
Though art's hid causes are not found,
All is not sweet, all is not sound.

Give me a look, give me a face
That makes simplicity a grace;
Robes loosely flowing, hair as free:
Such sweet neglect more taketh me,
Than all th'adulteries of art,
That strike mine eyes, but not my heart.

BEN JONSON (1572–1637)

(b)

THE CLOD AND THE PEBBLE

'Love seeketh not itself to please,
Nor for itself hath any care,
But for another gives its ease,
And builds a Heaven in Hell's despair.'

So sung a little Clod of Clay,
Trodden with the cattle's feet,
But a Pebble of the brook
Warbled out these metres meet:

'Love seeketh only Self to please,
To bind another to its delight,
Joys in another's loss of ease,
And builds a Hell in Heaven's despite.'

WILLIAM BLAKE (1757–1827)

LOVE

The difficult part of love
Is being selfish enough,
Is having the blind persistence
To upset someone's existence
Just for your own sake—
What cheek it must take.

And then the unselfish side—
Who can be satisfied
Putting someone else first,
So that you come off worst?
My life is for me:
As well deny gravity.

Yet, vicious or virtuous,
Love still suits most of us;
Only the bleeder who
Can't manage either view
Is ever wholly rebuffed—
And he can get stuffed.

PHILIP LARKIN

(c)

HOLY SONNET

Batter my heart, three person'd God; for you
As yet but knocke, breathe, shine, and seeke to mend;
That I may rise, and stand, o'erthrow mee, and bend
Your force, to breake, blowe, burn and make me new.
I, like an usurpt towne, to'another due,
Labour to'admit you, but Oh, to no end,
Reason your viceroy in mee, mee should defend,
But is captiv'd, and proves weake or untrue.
Yet dearely'I love you, and would be lov'd faine,
But am betroth'd unto your enemie:
Divorce mee, 'untie, or breake that knot againe,
Take mee to you, imprison mee, for I
Except you'enthrall mee, never shall be free,
Nor ever chast, except you ravish mee.

JOHN DONNE (1572–1631)

THOU ART INDEED JUST, LORD

Thou art indeed just, Lord, if I contend
With thee; but, sir, so what I plead is just.
Why do sinners' ways prosper? and why must
Disappointment all I endeavour end?
    Wert thou my enemy, O thou my friend,
How wouldst thou worse, I wonder, than thou dost
Defeat, thwart me? Oh, the sots and thralls of lust
Do in spare hours more thrive than I that spend,
Sir, life upon thy cause. See, banks and brakes
Now, leavèd how thick! lacèd they are again
With fretty chervil, look, and fresh wind shakes
Them; birds build—but not I build; no, but strain,
Time's eunuch, and not breed one work that wakes.
Mine, O thou lord of life, send my roots rain.

GERARD MANLEY HOPKINS (1844–1889)

(d)

PIKE

Pike, three inches long, perfect
Pike in all part, green tigering the gold.
Killers from the egg: the malevolent aged grin.
They dance on the surface among the flies.

Or move, stunned by their own grandeur,
Over a bed of emerald, silhouette
Of submarine delicacy and horror.
A hundred feet long in their world.

In ponds, under the heat-struck lily pads—
Gloom of their stillness:
Logged on last year's black leaves, watching upwards.
Or hung in an amber cavern of weeds

The jaws' hooked clamp and fangs
Not to be changed at this date;
A life subdued to its instrument;
The gills kneading quietly, and the pectorals.

Three we kept behind glass,
Jungled in weed: three inches, four,
And four and a half: fed fry to them—
Suddenly there were two. Finally one

With a sag belly and the grin it was born with.
And indeed they spare nobody.
Two, six pounds each, over two feet long,
High and dry and dead in the willow-herb—

One jammed past its gills down the other's gullet:
The outside eye stared: as a vice locks—
The same iron in this eye
Though its film shrank in death.

A pond I fished, fifty yards across,
Whose lilies and muscular tench
Had outlasted every visible stone
Of the monastery that planted them—

Stilled legendary depth:
It was as deep as England. It held
Pike too immense to stir, so immense and old
That past nightfall I dared not cast

But silently cast and fished
With the hair frozen on my head
For what might move, for what eye might move.
The still splashes on the dark pond.

Owls hushing the floating woods
Frail on my ear against the dream
Darkness beneath night's darkness had freed,
That rose slowly towards me, watching.

TED HUGHES

THE PIKE

From shadows of rich oaks outpeer
The moss-green bastions of the weir,
Where the quick dipper forages
In elver-peopled crevices,
And a small runlet trickling down the sluice
Gossamer music tires not to unloose.

Else round the broad pool's hush
    Nothing stirs,
Unless sometime a straggling heifer crush
Through the thronged spinney where the pheasant whirs;
    Or martins in a flash
Come with wild mirth to dip their magical wings,
While in the shallow some doomed bulrush swings
At whose hid root the diver vole's teeth gnash.

And nigh this toppling reed, still as the dead
    The great pike lies, the murderous patriarch
    Watching the waterpit sheer-shelving dark,
Where through the plash his lithe bright vassals thread.

The rose-finned roach and bluish bream
And staring ruffe steal up the stream
Hard by their glutted tyrant, now
Still as a sunken bough.

He on the sandbank lies,
    Sunning himself long hours
With stony gorgon eyes:
    Westward the hot sun lowers.

Sudden the gray pike changes, and quivering poises for slaughter;
    Intense terror wakens around him, the shoals scud awry, but there chances
    A chub unsuspecting; the prowling fins quicken, in fury he lances;
And the miller that opens the hatch stands amazed at the whirl in the water.

EDMUND BLUNDEN

(e)

REVELATION

I remember once being shown the black bull
when a child at the farm for eggs and milk.
They called him Bob—as though perhaps
you could reduce a monster
with the charm of a friendly name.
At the threshold of his outhouse, someone
held my hand and let me peer inside.
At first, only black
and the hot reek of him. Then he was immense,
his edges merging with the darkness, just
a big bulk and a roar to be really scared of,
a trampling, and a clanking tense with the chain's jerk.
His eyes swivelled in the great wedge of his tossed head.
He roared his rage. His nostrils gaped.

And in the yard outside,
oblivious hens picked their way about.
The faint and rather festive tinkling
behind the mellow stone and hasp was all they knew
of that Black Mass, straining at his chains.
I had always half-known he existed—
this antidote and Anti-Christ his anarchy
threatening the eggs, well rounded, self-contained—
and the placidity of milk.

I ran, my pigtails thumping on my back in fear,
past the big boys in the farm lane
who pulled the wings from butterflies and
blew up frogs with straws.
Past throned hedge and harried nest,
scared of the eggs shattering—
only my small and shaking hand on the jug's rim
in case the milk should spill.

LIZ LOCHHEAD

THE BULL MOSES

A hoist up and I could lean over
The upper edge of the high half-door,
My left foot ledged on the hinge, and look in at the byre's
Blaze of darkness: a sudden shut-eyed look
Backward into the head.

   Blackness is depth
Beyond star. But the warm weight of his breathing,
The ammoniac reek of his litter, the hotly-tongued
Mash of his cud, steamed against me.
Then, slowly, as onto the mind's eye—
The brow like masonry, the deep-keeled neck:
Something came up there onto the brink of the gulf,
Hadn't heard of the world, too deep in itself to be called to,
Stood in sleep. He would swing his muzzle at a fly
But the square of sky where I hung, shouting, waving,
Was nothing to him; nothing of our light
Found any reflection in him.

   Each dusk the farmer led him
Down to the pond to drink and smell the air,
And he took no pace but the farmer
Led him to take it, as if he knew nothing
Of the ages and continents of his fathers,
Shut, while he wombed, to a dark shed
And steps between his door and the duckpond;
The weight of the sun and the moon and the world hammered
To a ring of brass through his nostrils.

   He would raise
His streaming muzzle and look out over the meadows,
But the grasses whispered nothing awake, the fetch
Of the distance drew nothing to momentum
In the locked black of his powers. He came strolling gently back.
Paused neither towards the pig-pens on his right,
Nor towards the cow-byres on his left: something
Deliberate in his leisure, some beheld future
Founding in his quiet.

   I kept the door wide,
Closed it after him and pushed the bolt.

TED HUGHES

WORKSHOP

POEMS TO COMPARE

As part of coursework or in preparation for an exam you may be asked to choose two poems on the same topic to compare or you may be given two poems you have never seen before and asked to write about their similarities and differences. This can be quite a daunting task unless you think about: (i) what the question is looking for, (ii) how you approach the reading of the poems and (iii) how you organise your answer. Do you, for example, write two short essays and put them together or do you flit back and forth between the two poems?

PREPARATION

A four phase approach is suggested:

(i) Read each of the poems once to give you an overall sense of the theme, how the writer handles it and the nature of the relationship between the two poems.
(ii) Re-read the first poem and make quick jottings on the poem: ideally (but only if it is a copy) jot around it on the pages circling and underlining as you go.

— Note particular images, ideas and feelings that strike you and say why.
— Note the kind of language used, technical points such as the use of alliteration, word-play, a particular rhythm, a particular rhyme scheme (or absence of it). It can help to say the poem over to yourself and to *hear* the sound of the words in your head.
— Note if the poem takes a particular form and why you think the writer has chosen to write it this way. It helps to look at the poem as an object for a moment: is its shape, for example, a compact and ordered sonnet, or meandering free verse with no tight structure or neat couplets . . . something else?
— Look for and note repeated or linked patterns of words, sounds, images as the poem unfolds.
— Look to see if a line of argument is developed in the poem. Does it move towards a conclusion, a point of view at the end?

Re-read the second poem and go through the same process.
(iii) Jot down what you feel is unique to each poem and give your reasons for saying so. Probably no more than three or four lines here to 'capture' each poem.
(iv) List the main points of similarity and difference between the two poems. Ask yourself whether the two writers have similar or different attitudes towards their subject.

WRITING UP

If you have used the four phase approach above then that preparation should help you to structure your essay:

● Begin with an opening paragraph based upon (iii) above, which captures the quality and the nature of each of the two poems.

● Follow up with several paragraphs based on (ii) above, which bring out the details you noticed in the reading of the poems. It is probably best to concentrate first on one poem and then on the other, just as you did in the note-making.

● Write a final paragraph based upon (iv) above, which discusses the main points of similarity and difference and, if appropriate, indicates the reasons for your preference of one poem over the other.

PART C

TEN POETS

THE DETAILS OF SHAKESPEARE'S life are sketchy. He was born in Stratford-upon-Avon and is thought to have attended the grammar school there where he would have gained a reasonable knowledge of Latin. He did not go on to University; and the first reliable record of his life after his christening is of his marriage in 1582 to Anne Hathaway. The Shakespeares had three children during the 1580s, including twins – a boy and a girl.

By 1592, Shakespeare was in London as an actor and playwright, notably with the most successful company, the Lord Chamberlain's Men which, in 1599, built the best known Elizabethan theatre, The Globe.

During the 1590s, Shakespeare wrote poetry (e.g. 'Venus and Adonis') and plays that were mainly either chronicle histories (e.g. *Richard II* and *Henry IV, parts i and ii*), or comedies (e.g. *A Midsummer Night's Dream* and *The Merchant of Venice*); the tragedy of *Romeo and Juliet* also dates from this time. Around the turn of the century, Shakespeare completed his cycle of histories with *Henry V* and wrote the great romantic comedies, *As You Like It*, *Twelfth Night*, and *Much Ado About Nothing*. The first decade of the seventeenth century was the period of the great tragedies – *Hamlet*, *Macbeth*, *King Lear*, and *Othello*. About 1610, Shakespeare appears to have retired to Stratford

The new Globe theatre

The Globe

though he continued to write for the stage, with 'romances' such as *A Winter's Tale* and *The Tempest*, until his death in 1616.

Although Shakespeare's poetry is best known from his plays (which incorporate a great number of songs), he also composed the most elaborate sonnet sequence ever written in English (see also Part A, Unit 8), published in 1609. The identities of the person to whom the sequence is dedicated, a 'Master. W.H.' and of the 'dark lady' about whom some of the poems are written remain two unsolved mysteries to this day.

The selection of extracts and poems here can give only the faintest indication of the work of the greatest writer in the language. We have chosen three speeches which recall the theatre for which so much of Shakespeare's poetry was composed: the opening Chorus from *Henry V* exhorting us to imagine what the stage cannot show us; the equally famous extended metaphor of the stage on which man's 'seven ages' are played out; and Prospero's lines from *The Tempest* which play on the ideas of 'acting' and the 'globe' to suggest the impermanence of life. We have also included one of Shakespeare's songs—a dirge or funeral song spoken by two princes over the supposedly dead body of their sister Imogen; an extended piece of 'scene painting' – the English camp before the Battle of Agincourt; a poetic reflection on the need to temper justice with mercy; and three of the sonnets. This selection aims to give examples of the range and variety of Shakespeare's writing; it can easily be added to from other plays you may be studying.

OTHER POEMS

'O! FOR A MUSE OF FIRE'

O! for a Muse of fire, that would ascend
The brightest heaven of invention;
A kingdom for a stage, princes to act
And monarchs to behold the swelling scene.
Then should the war-like Harry, like himself,
Assume the port of Mars; and at his heels,
Leash'd in like hounds, should famine, sword, and fire
Crouch for employment. But pardon, gentles all,
The flat unraised spirits that hath dar'd
On this unworthy scaffold to bring forth
So great an object: can this cockpit hold
The vasty fields of France? or may we cram
Within this wooden O the very casques
That did affright the air at Agincourt?
O, pardon! since a crooked figure may
Attest in little place a million;
And let us, ciphers to this great accompt,
On your imaginary forces work.
Suppose within the girdle of these walls
Are now confin'd two mighty monarchies,
Whose high upreared and abutting fronts
The perilous narrow ocean parts asunder:
Piece out our imperfections with your thoughts:
Into a thousand parts divide one man,
And make imaginary puissance;
Think when we talk of horses that you see them
Printing their proud hoofs i' the receiving earth;
For 'tis your thoughts that now must deck our kings,
Carry them here and there, jumping o'er times,
Turning the accomplishment of many years
Into an hour-glass: for the which supply,
Admit me Chorus to this history;
Who prologue-like your humble patience pray,
Gently to hear, kindly to judge, our play.

Henry V, Prologue

BEFORE AGINCOURT

Now entertain conjecture of a time
When creeping murmur and the poring dark
Fills the wide vessel of the universe.
From camp to camp, through the foul womb of night,
The hum of either army stilly sounds,
That the fix'd sentinels almost receive
The secret whispers of each other's watch:
Fire answers fire, and through their paly flames
Each battle sees the other's umber'd face:
Steed threatens steed, in high and boastful neighs
Piercing the night's dull ear; and from the tents

The armourers, accomplishing the knights,
With busy hammers closing rivets up,
Give dreadful note of preparation.
The country cocks do crow, the clocks do toll,
And the third hour of drowsy morning name.
Proud of their numbers, and secure in soul,
The confident and over-lusty French
Do the low-rated English play at dice;
And chide the cripple tardy-gaited night
Who, like a foul and ugly witch, doth limp
So tediously away. The poor condemned English,
Like sacrifices, by their watchful fires
Sit patiently, and inly ruminate
The morning's danger, and their gesture sad
Investing lank-lean cheeks and war-worn coats
Presenteth them unto the gazing moon
So many horrid ghosts. O! now, who will behold
The royal captain of this ruin'd band
Walking from watch to watch, from tent to tent,
Let him cry 'Praise and glory on his head!'
For forth he goes and visits all his host,
Bids them good morrow with a modest smile,
And calls them brothers, friends, and countrymen.
Upon his royal face there is no note
How dread an army hath enrounded him;
Nor doth he dedicate one jot of colour
Unto the weary and all-watched night:
But freshly looks and overbears attaint
With cheerful semblance and sweet majesty;
That every wretch, pining and pale before,
Beholding him, plucks comfort from his looks.
A largess universal, like the sun
His liberal eye doth give to every one,
Thawing cold fear. Then mean and gentle all,
Behold, as may unworthiness define,
A little touch of Harry in the night.
And so our scene must to the battle fly;
Where,—O for pity,—we shall much disgrace,
With four or five most vile and ragged foils,
Right ill dispos'd in brawl ridiculous,
The name of Agincourt.

Henry V, Act 4 Chorus

THE SEVEN AGES OF MAN

All the world's a stage,
And all the men and women merely players:
They have their exits and their entrances;
And one man in his time plays many parts,
His acts being seven ages. At first the infant,
Mewling and puking in the nurse's arms.
And then the whining schoolboy, with his satchel,
And shining morning face, creeping like snail
Unwillingly to school. And then the lover,
Sighing like furnace, with a woeful ballad
Made to his mistress' eyebrow. Then a soldier,
Full of strange oaths, and bearded like the pard,
Jealous in honour, sudden and quick in quarrel,
Seeking the bubble reputation
Even in the cannon's mouth. And then the justice,
In fair round belly with good capon lin'd,
With eyes severe, and beard of formal cut,
Full of wise saws and modern instances;
And so he plays his part. The sixth age shifts
Into the lean and slipper'd pantaloon,
With spectacles on nose and pouch on side,
His youthful hose well sav'd, a world too wide
For his shrunk shank; and his big manly voice,
Turning again toward childish treble, pipes
And whistles in his sound. Last scene of all,
That ends this strange eventful history,
Is second childishness and mere oblivion,
Sans teeth, sans eyes, sans taste, sans everything.

As You Like It, Act 2 Scene 7

'THE QUALITY OF MERCY'

The quality of mercy is not strain'd,
It droppeth as the gentle rain from heaven
Upon the place beneath: it is twice bless'd;
It blesseth him that gives and him that takes:
'Tis mightiest in the mightiest; it becomes
The throned monarch better than his crown;
His sceptre shows the force of temporal power,
The attribute to awe and majesty,
Wherein doth sit the dread and fear of kings;
But mercy is above this sceptred sway,
It is enthroned in the hearts of kings,
It is an attribute to God himself,
And earthly power doth then show likest God's
When mercy seasons justice.

The Merchant of Venice, Act 4 Scene 1

'FEAR NO MORE THE HEAT O' THE SUN'

Fear no more the heat o' the sun,
    Nor the furious winter's rages;
Thou thy worldly task hast done,
    Home art gone, and ta'en thy wages;
Golden lads and girls all must
As chimney-sweepers, come to dust.

Fear no more the frown o' the great,
    Thou art past the tyrant's stroke:
Care no more to clothe and eat;
    To thee the reed is as the oak;
The sceptre, learning, physic, must
    All follow this, and come to dust.

Fear no more the lightning-flash,
    Nor the all-dreaded thunder-stone;
Fear not slander, censure rash;
    Thou hast finish'd joy and moan:
All lovers young, all lovers must
    Consign to thee, and come to dust.

No exorcizer harm thee!
    Nor no witchcraft charm thee!
Ghost unlaid forbear thee!
    Nothing ill come near thee!
Quiet consummation have;
    And renowned be thy grave!

Cymbeline, Act 4 Scene 2

'OUR REVELS NOW ARE ENDED'

Our revels now are ended. These our actors,
As I foretold you, were all spirits and
Are melted into air, into thin air:
And, like the baseless fabric of this vision,
The cloud-capp'd towers, the gorgeous palaces,
The solemn temples, the great globe itself,
Yea, all which it inherit, shall dissolve
And, like this insubstantial pageant faded,
Leave not a rack behind. We are such stuff
As dreams are made on, and our little life
Is rounded with a sleep.

The Tempest, Act 4 Scene 1

SONNET 18

Shall I compare thee to a summer's day?
Thou art more lovely and more temperate.
Rough winds do shake the darling buds of May,
And summer's lease hath all too short a date.
Sometime too hot the eye of heaven shines,
And often is his gold complexion dimmed;
And every fair from fair sometime declines,
By chance or nature's changing course untrimmed.
But thy eternal summer shall not fade,
Nor lose possession of that fair thou ow'st,
Nor shall Death brag thou wand'rest in his shade,
When in eternal lines to time thou grow'st.
   So long as men can breathe or eyes can see,
   So long lives this, and this gives life to thee.

SONNET 29

When, in disgrace with Fortune and men's eyes,
I all alone beweep my outcast state,
And trouble deaf heaven with my bootless cries,
And look upon myself and curse my fate,
Wishing me like to one more rich in hope,
Featured like him, like him with friends possessed,
Desiring this man's art, and that man's scope,
With what I most enjoy contented least;
Yet, in these thoughts myself almost despising,
Haply I think on thee, and then my state,
Like to the lark at break of day arising
From sullen earth, sings hymns at heaven's gate;
   For thy sweet love remembered such wealth brings
   That then I scorn to change my state with kings.

SONNET 71

No longer mourn for me when I am dead
Than you shall hear the surly sullen bell
Give warning to the world that I am fled
From this vile world with vilest worms to dwell.
Nay, if you read this line, remember not
The hand that writ it, for I love you so
That I in your sweet thoughts would be forgot
If thinking on me then should make you woe.
O, if, I say, you look upon this verse,
When I, perhaps, compounded am with clay,
Do not so much as my poor name rehearse,
But let your love even with my life decay;
   Lest the wise world should look into your moan,
   And mock you with me after I am gone.

1757–1827

WILLIAM BLAKE WAS A Londoner who had little formal education, except in Art when he went to drawing school at the age of ten and, later, when he studied at the school of the Royal Academy of Arts. He started a seven-year apprenticeship to an engraver at the age of 14, began to write poetry and read widely in his teens, married when he was 24, and had his first book of poems, *Poetical Sketches* (from which the 'Song', p. 148, is taken), printed two years later.

In 1788, Blake began to experiment with what he called 'illuminated printing', a method he subsequently used to produce most of his books of combined poems and designs. Clearly, Blake conceived of each poem-picture as an artistic unity. He both wrote the words (in reverse, so that when printed they would appear normally) and drew the illustration directly on to copper plate using an acid-resistant medium. Then, he etched the plate in acid to eat away the rest of the copper, leaving the design standing out in relief. Finally, he printed the pages from these plates, coloured them by hand, assembled the pages, and bound them into a book.

All the poems on pp. 148–151 from his *Songs of Innocence and Experience* were produced in this labour-intensive way. While this means that each copy of the *Songs* is uniquely coloured, it also means that there were few printed – just 28 copies are thought to exist. Such time-consuming effort to make these illuminated books suggests that Blake wanted those who looked *at* them also to look *into* them, to experience the two arts simultaneously, to be both readers and spectators. The black and white pictures alongside some of the poems in this section give an idea of Blake's images; but try to look at the edition of the *Songs* edited by Sir Geoffrey Keynes (OUP) with its colour reproductions.

Though each poem stands independently, a number of the songs of innocence have a counterpart in the songs of experience. This selection contains such a pairing: 'Infant Joy' and 'Infant Sorrow'. Blake's 'Tyger', one of the best-known poems in the language, is a series of questions confronting the puzzle of Creation which may be condensed into a single question: 'How can it be that God created power and evil as well as gentleness and good?' 'The Sick Rose', too, works symbolically and offers, perhaps, the clearest opportunity to 'read' the illustration as well as the poem. The theme of love is given a different treatment in 'The Garden of Love'. The last two poems show other characteristics of Blake's verse. 'London', one of his grimmest poems, uses several symbolic figures and compresses images of fear, poverty, disease, prostitution and repression into a nightmare vision. 'A Poison Tree', by contrast, with its echoes of Eden, is more of a moral fable, a character it shares with the poem by Blake on p. 132, 'The Clod and the Pebble'.

WILLIAM BLAKE

OTHER POEMS

SONG

How sweet I roam'd from field to field,
  And tasted all the summer's pride,
'Til I the prince of love beheld,
  Who in the sunny beams did glide!

He shew'd me lilies for my hair,
  And blushing roses for my brow;
He led me through his gardens fair,
  Where all his golden pleasures grow.

With sweet May dews my wings were wet,
  And Phœbus fir'd my vocal rage;
He caught me in his silken net,
  And shut me in his golden cage.

He loves to sit and hear me sing,
  Then, laughing, sports and plays with me;
Then stretches out my golden wing,
  And mocks my loss of liberty.

THE SMILE

There is a Smile of Love,
And there is a Smile of Deceit,
And there is a Smile of Smiles
In which these two Smiles meet.

And there is a Frown of Hate,
And there is a Frown of Disdain,
And there is a Frown of Frowns
Which you strive to forget in vain,

For it sticks in the Heart's deep Core
And it sticks in the deep Back bone;
And no Smile that ever was smil'd,
But only one Smile alone,

That betwixt the Cradle & Grave
It only once Smil'd can be;
But, when it once is Smil'd,
There's an end to all Misery.

from: AUGURIES OF INNOCENCE

To see a World in a Grain of Sand
And a Heaven in a Wild Flower,
Hold Infinity in the palm of your hand
And Eternity in an hour.

A Robin Red breast in a Cage
Puts all Heaven in a Rage.
A dove house fill'd with doves & Pigeons
Shudders Hell thro' all its regions.
A dog starv'd at his Master's Gate
Predicts the ruin of the State.
A Horse misus'd upon the Road
Calls to Heaven for Human blood.
Each outcry of the hunted Hare
A fibre from the Brain does tear.
A Skylark wounded in the wing,
A Cherubim does cease to sing.

INFANT JOY

I have no name
I am but two days old.—
What shall I call thee?
I happy am
Joy is my name,—
Sweet joy befall thee!

Pretty joy!
Sweet joy but two days old.
Sweet joy I call thee:
Thou dost smile.
I sing the while
Sweet joy befall thee.

INFANT SORROW

My mother groand! my father wept.
Into the dangerous world I leapt:
Helpless, naked, piping loud:
Like a fiend hid in a cloud.

Struggling in my fathers hands:
Striving against my swadling bands:
Bound and weary I thought best
To sulk upon my mothers breast.

THE SICK ROSE

O Rose thou art sick.
The invisible worm,
That flies in the night
In the howling storm:

Has found out thy bed
Of crimson joy:
And his dark secret love
Does thy life destroy.

THE TYGER

Tyger Tyger, burning bright,
In the forests of the night;
What immortal hand or eye,
Could frame thy fearful symmetry?

In what distant deeps or skies,
Burnt the fire of thine eyes?
On what wings dare he aspire?
What the hand, dare sieze the fire?

And what shoulder, & what art,
Could twist the sinews of thy heart?
And when thy heart began to beat,
What dread hand? & what dread feet?

What the hammer? what the chain,
In what furnace was thy brain?
What the anvil? what dread grasp,
Dare its deadly terrors clasp?

When the stars threw down their spears
And water'd heaven with their tears:
Did he smile his work to see?
Did he who made the Lamb make thee?

Tyger Tyger burning bright,
In the forests of the night:
What immortal hand or eye,
Dare frame thy fearful symmetry?

THE GARDEN OF LOVE

I went to the Garden of Love.
And saw what I never had seen:
A Chapel was built in the midst,
Where I used to play on the green.

And the gates of this Chapel were shut,
And Thou shalt not, writ over the door;
So I turn'd to the Garden of Love,
That so many sweet flowers bore,

And I saw it was filled with graves,
And tomb-stones where flowers should be:
And Priests in black gowns, were walking their
rounds,
And binding with briars, my joys & desires.

LONDON

I wander thro' each charter'd street,
Near where the charter'd Thames does flow
And mark in every face I meet
Marks of weakness, marks of woe.

In every cry of every Man,
In every Infants cry of fear,
In every voice; in every ban,
The mind-forg'd manacles I hear

How the Chimney-sweepers cry
Every blackning Church appalls,
And the hapless Soldiers sigh
Runs in blood down Palace walls

But most thro' midnight streets I hear
How the youthful Harlots curse
Blasts the new-born Infants tear
And blights with plagues the Marriage hearse.

A POISON TREE

I was angry with my friend:
I told my wrath, my wrath did end.
I was angry with my foe:
I told it not, my wrath did grow.

And I waterd it in fears,
Night & morning with my tears:
And I sunned it with smiles,
And with soft deceitful wiles.

And it grew both day and night,
Till it bore an apple bright.
And my foe beheld it shine,
And he knew that it was mine.

And into my garden stole,
When the night had veild the pole;
In the morning glad I see,
My foe outstretchd beneath the tree.

I T IS NOT EASY to look at the portrait of Wordsworth in his later years, aged 72, and reconcile that sober, thoughtful face with the young man who, 50 years earlier, had allied himself with great fervour to the ideals of the French Revolution, had an affair with a young French woman and returned to England to write, before he was 30, some of the most influential poems in the English language.

William Wordsworth was born at Cockermouth in the Lake District, went to grammar school in Hawkshead and later to St John's College, Cambridge. In his early twenties he went on a walking tour in Europe and was very much excited and influenced by the ideas and ideals of the French Revolution. It was at about this time that he began writing seriously and realised he was destined to be a poet.

To a young man, from a fairly sheltered background, abroad for the first time, the turmoil and the promise of the Revolution were intoxicating. The old order was overthrown and it seemed a time full of hope and re-birth. In one of his poems he describes

> **France standing on the top of golden hours,**
> **And human nature seeming born again.**

He mixed easily with the ordinary people of France and saw himself as a Patriot, with liberal and republican views and sympathetic to the plight of the common man or woman.

It was perhaps the time of his life when he lived most intensely and, whilst in France, he fell in love with Annette Vallon, the daughter of a French surgeon. Annette bore him a daughter, though they were to part on Wordsworth's return to England in 1792. The sonnet 'Composed Upon Westminster Bridge' was written when he was on his way to France in 1802, returning to see Annette and Caroline, his daughter, by now ten years old. The sonnet 'It is a Beauteous Evening' was com-

posed on the beach near Calais and Caroline is the 'Dear Child' who walks with him on the beach.

Wordsworth's commitment to what had seemed a glorious Revolution was shaken by the atrocities of the terrors that were to follow. For some time after his return to England in 1792 he was under severe emotional strain and his beliefs sorely tested: he had lost his way in life. It was his devoted sister, Dorothy, who helped resolve the crisis. She had always been close to him and he settled with her in Somerset. Later in the year Dorothy and William met the poet Samuel Taylor Coleridge and the three became so close that they were described as 'three persons in one soul'. During this period and under the watchful eye of Dorothy, who loved him dearly and was a direct link to happier times in his childhood,

Wordsworth began to regain his own happiness.

A new impetus was given to his writing by his association with Coleridge and together in 1798 they published one of the most important works in English literature, *Lyrical Ballads*. One aim of *Lyrical Ballads* was to get away from the elaborate and highly artificial style of poetry which had become the norm, and for poems to use instead 'the language really used by men'. Another aim was to make the personal feelings expressed by lyric poets as acceptable a subject for poetry as the grand themes and styles of earlier poets. Further, Wordsworth stated that 'incidents and subjects from common life' were fit subjects for art – something which today presents no problem but which in his day was revolutionary. Wordsworth, said Coleridge, wanted his readers to awake to 'the loveliness and the wonder of the world before us', to see what we had taken as commonplace with new eyes.

The simplest things in Nature could give rise to profound thoughts and, in Wordsworth's view, as we look afresh at them, seeing through the poet's eyes, we begin to feel a deeper understanding of the world, and our place in it, and learn more of ourselves and our relationship with Nature and with God. Wordsworth's poetry increasingly became more concerned with the power of the natural world and with a mystical sense of God in all things. Already in his poem 'Tintern Abbey' which appears in *Lyrical Ballads*, this profound pantheism is apparent as, for example, when he writes of experiencing

> —a sense sublime
> Of something far more deeply interfused,
> Whose dwelling is the light of setting suns
> And the round ocean and the living air,
> And the blue sky, and in the mind of man;
> A motion and a spirit that impels
> All thinking things, all objects of all thought,
> And rolls through all things.

Wordsworth and Dorothy moved back to live at Dove Cottage, Grasmere in the Lake District in 1799 and the stream of superb poems continued unabated for the next ten years. The 1804 poem 'I Wandered Lonely as a Cloud', known to generations of school children simply as 'Daffodils', picks up a particularly sharp piece of observation by Dorothy Wordsworth which she first recorded in her Journal (see p. 156). William turns it into a poem which invites us to share, quite literally, the wealth of the experience and reflect on what Nature can offer us.

Wordsworth saw his own idyllic childhood among the lakes and lonely hills as profoundly influencing his understanding, almost as though he saw Nature shaping his thoughts and character. The two extracts 'Stealing a Boat' and 'Skating' taken from his long poem *The Prelude*, begun in 1799, show aspects of this belief. Notice how, when he steals the boat, the hills themselves seem to rise up and accuse him of his crime: Nature is, it seems, taking a hand in shaping his character. The childhood skating episode, described as a 'happy time' and for Wordsworth 'a time of Rapture!' captures his overwhelming sense of being a part of the earth's motion when he stops short on his skates and feels the earth wheel past him.

Wordsworth wrote on into old age but never perhaps regained the intensity, simplicity and flashes of insight of these earlier poems, perhaps because as he aged he was moving further away from the wellspring of his own inspiration.

OTHER POEMS

'The Kitten and Falling Leaves'   p. 123

STEALING A BOAT

   One summer evening (led by her) I found
A little Boat tied to a Willow-tree
Within a rocky cave, its usual home.
Strait I unloosed her chain, and, stepping in,
Pushed from the shore. It was an act of stealth
And troubled pleasure, nor without the voice
Of mountain-echoes did my Boat move on,
Leaving behind her still, on either side,
Small circles glittering idly in the moon,
Until they melted all into one track
Of sparkling light. But now, like one who rows
(Proud of his skill) to reach a chosen point
With an unswerving line, I fixed my view
Upon the summit of a craggy ridge,
The horizon's utmost boundary; for above
Was nothing but the stars and the grey sky.
She was an elfin Pinnace; lustily
I dipped my oars into the silent lake;
And, as I rose upon the stroke, my boat
Went heaving through the Water like a swan:
When, from behind that craggy Steep, till then
The horizon's bound, a huge peak, black and huge,
As if with voluntary power instinct,
Upreared its head.—I struck, and struck again,
And, growing still in stature, the grim Shape
Towered up between me and the stars, and still,
For so it seemed, with purpose of its own
And measured motion, like a living Thing
Strode after me. With trembling oars I turned,
And through the silent water stole my way
Back to the Covert of the Willow-tree;
There, in her mooring-place, I left my Bark,—
And through the meadows homeward went, in grave
And serious mood; but after I had seen
That spectacle, for many days, my brain
Worked with a dim and undetermined sense
Of unknown modes of being; o'er my thoughts
There hung a darkness, call it solitude
Or blank desertion. No familiar Shapes
Remained, no pleasant images of trees,
Of sea or Sky, no colours of green fields,
But huge and mighty Forms, that do not live
Like living men, moved slowly through the mind
By day, and were a trouble to my dreams.

From: The Prelude, Book 1

SKATING

    —And in the frosty season, when the sun
Was set, and visible for many a mile,
The cottage windows blazed through twilight gloom,
I heeded not their summons;—happy time
It was indeed for all of us; for me
It was a time of rapture!—Clear and loud
The village Clock toll'd six—I wheeled about,
Proud and exulting like an untired horse
That cares not for his home.—All shod with steel,
We hissed along the polished ice, in games
Confederate, imitative of the chase
And woodland pleasures,—the resounding horn,
The Pack loud-chiming and the hunted hare.
So through the darkness and the cold we flew,
And not a voice was idle: with the din
Smitten, the precipices rang aloud;
The leafless trees and every icy crag
Tinkled like iron; while far distant hills
Into the tumult sent an alien sound
Of melancholy, not unnoticed while the stars,
Eastward, were sparkling clear, and in the west
The orange sky of evening died away.
Not seldom from the uproar I retired
Into a silent bay,—or sportively
Glanced sideway, leaving the tumultuous throng
To cut across the reflex of a star
That fled, and, flying still before me, gleamed
Upon the glassy plain: and oftentimes,
When we had given our bodies to the wind,
And all the shadowy banks on either side
Came sweeping through the darkness, spinning still
The rapid line of motion, then at once
Have I, reclining back upon my heels,
Stopped short; yet still the solitary cliffs
Wheeled by me—even as if the earth had rolled
With visible motion her diurnal round!
Behind me did they stretch in solemn train,
Feebler and feebler, and I stood and watched
Till all was tranquil as a dreamless sleep.

from: The Prelude, Book 1

COMPOSED UPON WESTMINSTER BRIDGE, SEPTEMBER 3, 1802

Earth has not any thing to show more fair:
Dull would he be of soul who could pass by
A sight so touching in its majesty:
This City now doth, like a garment, wear
The beauty of the morning; silent, bare,
Ships, towers, domes, theatres, and temples lie
Open unto the fields, and to the sky;
All bright and glittering in the smokeless air.
Never did sun more beautifully steep
In his first splendour, valley, rock, or hill;
Ne'er saw I, never felt, a calm so deep!
The river glideth at his own sweet will:
Dear God! the very houses seem asleep;
And all that mighty heart is lying still!

IT IS A BEAUTEOUS EVENING

It is a beauteous evening, calm and free,
The holy time is quiet as a Nun
Breathless with adoration; the broad sun
Is sinking down in its tranquility;
The gentleness of heaven broods o'er the Sea:
Listen! the mighty Being is awake,
And doth with his eternal motion make
A sound like thunder—everlastingly.
Dear Child! dear Girl! that walkest with me here,
If thou appear untouched by solemn thought,
Thy nature is not therefore less divine:
Thou liest in Abraham's bosom[1] all the year,
And worship'st at the Temple's inner shrine[2],
God being with thee when we know it not.

[1] Where souls in heaven rest   [2] Where God is present

from: THE GRASMERE JOURNALS

Apr. 15. It was a threatening misty morning—but mild. We set off after dinner from Eusemere. Mrs. Clarkson went a short way with us but turned back. The wind was furious and we thought we must have returned. We first rested in the large Boat-house, then under a furze Bush opposite Mr. Clarkson's. Saw the plough going in the field. The wind seized our breath the Lake was rough. There was a Boat by itself floating in the middle of the Bay below Water Millock. We rested again in the Water Millock Lane. The hawthorns are black and green, the birches here and there greenish but there is yet more of purple to be seen on the Twigs. We got over into a field to avoid some cows— people working, a few primroses by the roadside, wood-sorrel flower, the anemone, scentless violets, strawberries, and that starry yellow flower which Mrs. C. called pile wort. When we were in the woods beyond Gowbarrow park we saw a few daffodils close to the water side. We fancied that the lake had floated the seeds ashore and that the little colony had so sprung up. But as we went along there were more and yet more and at last under the boughs of the trees, we saw that there was a long belt of them along the shore, about the breadth of a country turnpike road. I never saw daffodils so beautiful they grew among the mossy stones about and about them, some rested their heads upon these stones as on a pillow for weariness and the rest tossed and reeled and danced and seemed as if they verily laughed with the wind that blew upon them over the lake, they looked so gay ever glancing ever changing. This wind blew directly over the lake to them. There was here and there a little knot and a few stragglers a few yards higher up but they were so few as not to disturb the simplicity and unity and life of that one busy highway.

DOROTHY WORDSWORTH

I WANDERED LONELY AS A CLOUD

I wandered lonely as a cloud
That floats on high o'er vales and hills,
When all at once I saw a crowd,
A host, of golden daffodils;
Beside the lake, beneath the trees,
Fluttering and dancing in the breeze.

Continuous as the stars that shine
And twinkle on the milky way,
They stretched in never-ending line
Along the margin of a bay:
Ten thousand saw I at a glance,
Tossing their heads in sprightly dance.

The waves beside them danced; but they
Out-did the sparkling waves in glee:
A poet could not but be gay,
In such a jocund company:
I gazed—and gazed—but little thought
What wealth the show to me had brought:

For oft, when on my couch I lie
In vacant or in pensive mood,
They flash upon that inward eye
Which is the bliss of solitude;
And then my heart with pleasure fills,
And dances with the daffodils.

STRANGE FITS OF PASSION
HAVE I KNOWN

Strange fits of passion have I known:
And I will dare to tell,
But in the Lover's ear alone,
What once to me befel.

When she I loved looked every day
Fresh as a rose in June,
I to her cottage bent my way,
Beneath an evening moon.

Upon the moon I fixed my eye,
All over the wide lea;
With quickening pace my horse drew nigh
Those paths so dear to me.

And now we reached the orchard-plot;
And, as we climbed the hill,
The sinking moon to Lucy's cot
Came near, and nearer still.

In one of those sweet dreams I slept,
Kind Nature's gentlest boon!
And all the while my eyes I kept
On the descending moon.

My horse moved on; hoof after hoof
He raised, and never stopped:
When down behind the cottage roof,
At once, the bright moon dropped.

What fond and wayward thoughts will slide
Into a Lover's head!
'O mercy!' to myself I cried,
'If Lucy should be dead!'

SHE DWELT AMONG THE
UNTRODDEN WAYS

She dwelt among the untrodden ways
    Beside the springs of Dove,
A Maid whom there were none to praise
    And very few to love:

A violet by a mossy stone
    Half hidden from the eye!
—Fair as a star, when only one
    Is shining in the sky.

She lived unknown, and few could know
    When Lucy ceased to be;
But she is in her grave, and, oh,
    The difference to me!

1830–1894

CHRISTINA ROSSETTI WAS PART of an Anglo-Italian family which had strong religious convictions and a love of the arts. These two influences profoundly affected both her life and her writing. She lived quietly, occupying her time with charitable work, with caring for her family and with writing poetry. She never married, though on two occasions her religious principles led to her breaking off plans to do so. Her brother, Dante Gabriel Rossetti was one of that group of painters and writers known as The Pre-Raphaelite Brotherhood whose work flourished particularly in the decade 1850–1860. In their deceptively simple lyric style, many of the poems in Christina Rossetti's first book, *Goblin Market and Other Poems* (1862) reflect the early aims of the Pre-Raphaelites to be true to nature and to depict it, whether in painting or language, in precise and minute detail. These qualities are most clearly seen in her poem 'Spring', p. 162.

While the tone of her poetry may often seem coloured by sadness and regret, frequently bringing together the themes of death and love ('Song', 'Remember'), its range covers a variety of styles. The selection here includes sonnets, lyric verse, narrative fable, devotional verse, song and even a Christmas carol. These poems show a number of different concerns: an awareness of gender that leads her to comment on the conventional representation of women in her brother's paintings ('In An Artist's Studio'); a strong belief in the after-life ('Uphill'); and, perhaps, most revealing of all in 'Winter: My Secret', the idea of protecting a secret inner space for herself behind a cover of playful humour. But, if the themes of her poetry are important, so is its music. Christina Rossetti's poems particularly need to be heard: one or two readings of, say, 'Song' or 'Remember' and the lines begin to lodge in the mind – an indication of her gift for using words with the precision and completeness of musical notes.

CHRISTINA ROSSETTI

CHRISTINA ROSSETTI

Pencil sketch of Elizabeth Siddal, Dante Gabriel Rossetti, Tate Gallery.

IN AN ARTIST'S STUDIO

One face looks out from all his canvases,
    One selfsame figure sits or walks or leans:
    We found her hidden just behind those screens,
That mirror gave back all her loveliness.
A queen in opal or in ruby dress,
    A nameless girl in freshest summer-greens,
    A saint, an angel—every canvas means
The same one meaning, neither more nor less.
He feeds upon her face by day and night,
    And she with true kind eyes looks back on him,
Fair as the moon and joyful as the light:
    Not wan with waiting, not with sorrow dim;
Not as she is, but was when hope shone bright;
    Not as she is, but as she fills his dream.

UP-HILL

Does the road wind up-hill all the way?
    Yes, to the very end.
Will the day's journey take the whole long day?
    From morn to night, my friend.

But is there for the night a resting-place?
    A roof for when the slow dark hours begin.
May not the darkness hide it from my face?
    You cannot miss that inn.

Shall I meet other wayfarers at night?
    Those who have gone before.
Then must I knock, or call when just in sight?
    They will not keep you standing at that door.

Shall I find comfort, travel-sore and weak?
    Of labour you shall find the sum.
Will there be beds for me and all who seek?
    Yea, beds for all who come.

SONG

When I am dead, my dearest,
    Sing no sad songs for me;
Plant thou no roses at my head,
    Nor shady cypress tree:
Be the green grass above me
    With showers and dewdrops wet;
And if thou wilt, remember,
    And if thou wilt, forget.
I shall not see the shadows,
    I shall not feel the rain;
I shall not hear the nightingale
    Sing on, as if in pain:
And dreaming through the twilight
    That doth not rise nor set,
Haply I may remember,
    And haply may forget.

SPRING

Frost-locked all the winter,
Seeds, and roots, and stones of fruits,
What shall make their sap ascend
That they may put forth shoots?
Tips of tender green,
Leaf, or blade, or sheath;
Telling of the hidden life
That breaks forth underneath,
Life nursed in its grave by Death.

Blows the thaw-wind pleasantly,
Drips the soaking rain,
By fits looks down the waking sun:
Young grass springs on the plain;
Young leaves clothe early hedgerow trees;
Seeds, and roots, and stones of fruits,
Swollen with sap put forth their shoots;
Curled-headed ferns sprout in the lane;
Birds sing and pair again.

There is no time like Spring,
When life's alive in everything,
Before new nestlings sing,
Before cleft swallows speed their journey back
Along the trackless track—
God guides their wing,
He spreads their table that they nothing lack,—
Before the daisy grows a common flower,
Before the sun has power
To scorch the world up in his noontide hour.

There is no time like Spring,
Like Spring that passes by:
There is no life like Spring-life born to die,—
Piercing the sod,
Clothing the uncouth clod,
Hatched in the nest,
Fledged on the windy bough,
Strong on the wing;
There is no time like Spring that passes by,
Now newly born, and now
Hastening to die.

A CHRISTMAS CAROL

In the bleak mid-winter
    Frosty wind made moan,
Earth stood hard as iron,
    Water like a stone;
Snow had fallen, snow on snow,
    Snow on snow,
In the bleak mid-winter
    Long ago.

Our God, Heaven cannot hold Him
    Nor earth sustain;
Heaven and earth shall flee away
    When He comes to reign;
In the bleak mid-winter
    A stable-place sufficed
The Lord God Almighty
    Jesus Christ.

Enough for Him, whom cherubim
    Worship night and day,
A breastful of milk
    And a mangerful of hay;
Enough for Him, whom angels
    Fall down before,
The ox and ass and camel
    Which adore.

Angels and archangels
    May have gathered there,
Cherubim and seraphim
    Thronged the air;
But only His mother
    In her maiden bliss
Worshipped the Beloved
    With a kiss.

What can I give Him,
    Poor as I am?
If I were a shepherd
    I would bring a lamb,
If I were a Wise Man
    I would do my part,—
Yet what I can I give Him,
    Give my heart.

REMEMBER

Sonnet

Remember me when I am gone away,
  Gone far away into the silent land;
  When you can no more hold me by the hand,
Nor I half turn to go yet turning stay.
Remember me when no more day by day
  You tell me of our future that you planned:
  Only remember me; you understand
It will be late to counsel then or pray.
Yet if you should forget me for a while
  And afterwards remember, do not grieve:
  For if the darkness and corruption leave
  A vestige of the thoughts that once I had,
Better by far you should forget and smile
  Than that you should remember and be sad.

THE WORLD

By day she woos me, soft, exceeding fair:
  But all night as the moon so changeth she;
  Loathsome and foul with hideous leprosy,
And subtle serpents gliding in her hair.
By day she woos me to the outer air,
  Ripe fruits, sweet flowers, and full satiety:
  But through the night a beast she grins at me,
A very monster void of love and prayer.
By day she stands a lie: by night she stands
  In all the naked horror of the truth,
With pushing horns and clawed and clutching hands.
Is this a friend indeed, that I should sell
  My soul to her, give her my life and youth,
Till my feet, cloven too, take hold on hell?

WHO SHALL DELIVER ME?

God strengthen me to bear myself;
That heaviest weight of all to bear,
Inalienable weight of care.

All others are outside myself;
I lock my door and bar them out,
The turmoil, tedium, gad-about.

I lock my door upon myself,
And bar them out; but who shall wall
Self from myself, most loathed of all?

If I could once lay down myself,
And start self-purged upon the race
That all must run! Death runs apace.

If I could set aside myself,
And start with lightened heart upon
The road by all men overgone!

God harden me against myself,
This coward with pathetic voice
Who craves for ease, and rest, and joys:

Myself, arch-traitor to myself;
My hollowest friend, my deadliest foe,
My clog whatever road I go.

Yet One there is can curb myself,
Can roll the strangling load from me,
Break off the yoke and set me free.

WINTER: MY SECRET

I tell my secret? No indeed, not I:
Perhaps some day, who knows?
But not today; it froze, and blows, and snows,
And you're too curious: fie!
You want to hear it? well:
Only, my secret's mine, and I won't tell.

Or, after all, perhaps there's none:
Suppose there is no secret after all,
But only just my fun.
Today's a nipping day, a biting day;
In which one wants a shawl,
A veil, a cloak, and other wraps:
I cannot ope to every one who taps,
And let the draughts come whistling thro' my hall;
Come bounding and surrounding me,
Come buffeting, astounding me,
Nipping and clipping thro' my wraps and all.
I wear my mask for warmth: who ever shows
His nose to Russian snows
To be pecked at by every wind that blows?
You would not peck? I thank you for good will,
Believe, but leave that truth untested still.

Spring's an expansive time: yet I don't trust
March with its peck of dust,
Nor April with its rainbow-crowned brief showers,
Nor even May, whose flowers
One frost may wither thro' the sunless hours.

Perhaps some languid summer day,
When drowsy birds sing less and less,
And golden fruit is ripening to excess,
If there's not too much sun nor too much cloud,
And the warm wind is neither still nor loud.
Perhaps my secret I may say,
Or you may guess.

1840–1928

T̲HE SON OF A̲ builder and born in Dorset, Thomas Hardy left school at 16 and was apprenticed to an architect. Although he practised as an architect himself, by the 1870s he was beginning to enjoy considerable success as a novelist with works such as *Far From The Madding Crowd*, *The Return of the Native*, and later, *The Mayor of Casterbridge*, *Tess of the D'Urbevilles* and *Jude the Obscure*. He had already established himself as a major novelist and was 58 years old before he stopped writing novels and published his first volume of poems. The poems in this first volume, unknown until it was published in 1898, had been written over a number of years, some as far back as 1865: poetry had been his first love as it was to be his last. For the rest of his life poetry was his vocation as a writer and he had published six further volumes of poems by his death in 1928.

The themes of his poems are often very similar to those of the novels. He had early lost his religious faith and although finding solace in his observation of the natural world and in the humour of the characters who populated his beloved 'Wessex', there is a sombre streak that runs through much of his work. He was very conscious of what he called 'life's little ironies' and the vagaries and disappointments of love – something of which he had personal experience as the poems on pp. 166–167 will testify.

His poems are as often as not themselves little stories or suggest a story untold. Many of his stories and poems such as 'The Convergence of the Twain' (p.169) which tells of the sinking of the *Titanic*, reflect what he saw as humanity's unending

struggle against the uncaring force that he felt ruled the world, but it would be wrong to see Hardy simply as a pessimist. True, he was often melancholy but he was also a man who knew what it was to be tender, to love and to be loved, to delight in music, the details of the natural world and the patterns of rustic life. His sad, thoughtful agnosticism as expressed in poems such as 'The Oxen' (p. 168) and 'The Darkling Thrush' (p. 167) speak across the century to many people today who cannot believe but are 'hoping it might be so.' More briskly, he challenges conventions in the poems published as *Satires of Circumstance* and in sharply focused pieces such as 'In Church' (p. 168) in which, he uncompromisingly exposes the humbug of the preacher.

To see Hardy's own valuation of himself and to have some sense of his fundamental gentleness, read his poem 'Afterwards' (p. 170) which tells us how he would like to be remembered.

OTHER POEMS

THOMAS *Hardy*

'WHEN I SET OUT FOR LYONNESSE'

(1870)

When I set out for Lyonnesse,
     A hundred miles away,
     The rime was on the spray,
And starlight lit my lonesomeness
When I set out for Lyonesse
     A hundred miles away.

What would bechance at Lyonnesse
     While I should sojourn there
     No prophet durst declare,
Nor did the wisest wizard guess
What would bechance at Lyonnesse
     While I should sojourn there.

When I came back from Lyonnesse
     With magic in my eyes,
     All marked with mute surmise
My radiance rare and fathomless,
When I came back from Lyonnesse
     With magic in my eyes!

A THUNDERSTORM IN TOWN

(A Reminiscence: 1893)

She wore a new 'terra-cotta' dress,
And we stayed, because of the pelting storm,
Within the hansom's dry recess,
Though the horse had stopped; yea, motionless
     We sat on, snug and warm.

Then the downpour ceased, to my sharp sad pain
And the glass that had screened our forms before
Flew up, and out she sprang to her door:
I should have kissed her if the rain
     Had lasted a minute more.

ON THE DEPARTURE PLATFORM

We kissed at the barrier; and passing through
She left me, and moment by moment got
Smaller and smaller, until to my view
      She was but a spot;

A wee white spot of muslin fluff
That down the diminishing platform bore
Through hustling crowds of gentle and rough
      To the carriage door.

Under the lamplight's fitful glowers,
Behind dark groups from far and near,
Whose interests were apart from ours,
      She would disappear,

Then show again, till I ceased to see
That flexible form, that nebulous white;
And she who was more than my life to me
      Had vanished quite. . . .

We have penned new plans since that fair fond day,
And in season she will appear again—
Perhaps in the same soft white array—
      But never as then!

—'And why, young man, must eternally fly
A joy you'll repeat, if you love her well?'
—O friend, nought happens twice thus; why,
      I cannot tell!

NEUTRAL TONES

We stood by a pond that winter day,
And the sun was white, as though chidden of God,
And a few leaves lay on the starving sod,
  —They had fallen from an ash, and were gray.

Your eyes on me were as eyes that rove
Over tedious riddles solved years ago;
And words played between us to and fro—
  On which lost the more by our love.

The smile on your mouth was the deadest thing
Alive enough to have strength to die;
And a grin of bitterness swept thereby
  Like an ominous bird-a-wing . . .

Since then, keen lessons that love deceives,
And wrings with wrong, have shaped to me
Your face, and the God-curst sun, and a tree,
  And a pond edged with grayish leaves.

THE DARKLING THRUSH

I leant upon a coppice gate
      When Frost was spectre-gray,
And Winter's dregs made desolate
      The weakening eye of day.
The tangled bine-stems scored the sky
      Like strings of broken lyres,
And all mankind that haunted nigh
      Had sought their household fires.

The land's sharp features seemed to be
      The Century's corpse outleant,
His crypt the Cloudy canopy,
      The wind his death-lament.
The ancient pulse of germ and birth
      Was shrunken hard and dry,
And every spirit upon earth
      Seemed fervourless as I.

At once a voice arose among
      The bleak twigs overhead
In a full-hearted evensong
      Of joy illimited;
An aged thrush, frail, gaunt, and small,
      In blast-beruffled plume,
Had chosen thus to fling his soul
      Upon the growing gloom.

So little cause for carolings
      Of such ecstatic sound
Was written on terrestrial things
      Afar or nigh around,
That I could think there trembled through
      His happy good-night air
Some blessed Hope, whereof he knew
      And I was unaware.

THE OXEN

CHRISTMAS EVE, and twelve of the clock.
    'Now they are all on their knees,'
An elder said as we sat in a flock
    By the embers in hearthside ease.

We pictured the meek mild creatures where
    They dwelt in their strawy pen,
Nor did it occur to one of us there
    To doubt they were kneeling then.

So fair a fancy few would weave
    In these years! Yet, I feel,
If someone said on Christmas Eve,
    'Come; see the oxen kneel

'In the lonely barton by yonder coomb
    Our childhood used to know,'
I should go with him in the gloom,
    Hoping it might be so.

IN CHURCH

'And now to God the Father', he ends,
And his voice thrills up to the topmost tiles:
Each listener chokes as he bows and bends,
And emotion pervades the crowded aisles.
Then the preacher glides to the vestry-door,
And shuts it, and thinks he is seen no more.

The door swings softly ajar meanwhile,
And a pupil of his in the Bible class,
Who adores him as one without gloss or guile,
Sees her idol stand with a satisfied smile
And re-enact at the vestry-glass
Each pulpit gesture in deft dumb-show
That had moved the congregation so.

THE RUINED MAID

'O'Melia, my dear, this does everything crown!
Who could have supposed I should meet you in Town?
And whence such fair garments, such prosperi-ty?'
'O didn't you know I'd been ruined?' said she.

'You left us in tatters, without shoes or socks,
Tired of digging potatoes, and spudding up docks;
And now you've gay bracelets and bright feathers three!'
'Yes: that's how we dress when we're ruined,' said she.

'At home in the barton[1] you said "thee" and "thou,"
And "thik oon," and "theäs oon," and "t'other"; but now
Your talking quite fits 'ee for high compa-ny!'
'Some polish is gained with one's ruin,' said she.

'Your hands were like paws then, your face blue and bleak
But now I'm bewitched by your delicate cheek,
And your little gloves fit as on any la-dy!'
'We never do work when we're ruined,' said she.

'You used to call home-life a hag-ridden dream,
And you'd sigh, and you'd sock; but at present you seem
To know not of megrims[2] or melancho-ly!'
'True. One's pretty lively when ruined,' said she.

'I wish I had feathers, a fine sweeping gown,
And a delicate face, and could strut about Town!'
'My dear—a raw country girl, such as you be,
Cannot quite expect that. You ain't ruined,' said she.

[1] farm [2] low spirits

AFTERWARDS

When the Present has latched its postern behind my tremulous stay,
    And the May month flaps its glad green leaves like wings,
Delicate-filmed as new-spun silk, will the neighbours say,
    'He was a man who used to notice such things'?

If it be in the dusk when, like an eyelid's soundless blink,
    The dewfall-hawk comes crossing the shades to alight
Upon the wind-warped upland thorn, a gazer may think,
    'To him this must have been a familiar sight.'

If I pass during some nocturnal blackness, mothy and warm,
    When the hedgehog travels furtively over the lawn,
One may say, 'He strove that such innocent creatures should come to no harm,
    But he could do little for them; and now he is gone.'

If, when hearing that I have been stilled at last, they stand at the door,
    Watching the full-starred heavens that winter sees,
Will this thought rise on those who will meet my face no more,
    'He was one who had an eye for such mysteries'?

And will any say when my bell of quittance is heard in the gloom,
    And a crossing breeze cuts a pause in its outrollings,
Till they rise again, as they were a new bell's boom,
    'He hears it not now, but used to notice such things'?

THE CONVERGENCE OF THE TWAIN

(*Lines on the loss of the* Titanic)

I

In a solitude of the sea
Deep from human vanity,
And the Pride of Life that planned her, stilly couches she

II

Steel chambers, late the pyres
Of her salamandrine fires,
Cold currents thrid, and turn to rhythmic tidal lyres.

III

Over the mirrors meant
To glass the opulent
The sea-worm crawls—grotesque, slimed, dumb, indifferent.

IV

Jewels in joy designed
To ravish the sensuous mind
Lie lightless, all their sparkles bleared and black and blind.

V

Dim moon-eyed fishes near
Gaze at the gilded gear
And query: 'What does this vaingloriousness down here?'

VI

Well: while was fashioning
This creature of cleaving wing,
The Immanent Will that stirs and urges everything

VII

Prepared a sinister mate
For her—so gaily great—
A Shape of Ice, for the time far and dissociate.

VIII

And as the smart ship grew
In stature, grace, and hue,
In shadowy silent distance grew the Iceberg too.

IX

Alien they seemed to be:
No mortal eye could see
The intimate welding of their later history,

X

Or sign that they were bent
By paths coincident
On being anon twin halves of one august event.

XI

Till the Spinner of the Years
Said 'Now!' And each one hears,
And consummation comes, and jars two hemispheres.

1874–1963

ROBERT FROST HAD SOME small success with poems in his teens and as a schoolboy felt he had a vocation as a poet. He graduated in 1895 and entered Harvard two years later. After trying various jobs he moved to New Hampshire as a farmer and continued to write. In 1912 he sold the farm and sailed for England with his wife and four children where he farmed for three years. In England he met most of the young poets of the day and published his first books of verse which soon won critical acclaim. In 1915 the family returned to America and farming, but writing and teaching increasingly claimed his time as he became one of the most sought after and celebrated of American poets. In 1961 he read one of his poems at President John F. Kennedy's inauguration.

His poems, although often seemingly simple, almost homely, on the surface and written in spare, clear language, may hide darker themes and hint at hidden menace. A poem, he said was 'a momentary stay against confusion.' No follower of literary fashion but true to his own, sometimes mystical, vision and his own characteristic voice, there is a quality in his verse which has stood the test of time.

The simplest thing – finding a spider; stopping by a wood on a snowy evening; seeing flowers dashed by the rain – can be the starting point for a poem which develops into what is almost a meditation. Other poems rely on the power of story and Frost's mastery of the rhythms of colloquial speech for their effect. In an easy, everyday voice he tells of his childhood memory of swinging on birch saplings, or of watching snow falling in the local woods. It is only afterwards that we realise how much more we have been told than just the story of the poem.

In 'The Road Not Taken' (p. 172) Frost tells of having to make a life-choice: we should be glad that he chose as he did.

OTHER POEMS

'Neither out Far nor in Deep'   p. 46

THE ROAD NOT TAKEN

Two roads diverged in a yellow wood,
And sorry I could not travel both
And be one traveller, long I stood
And looked down one as far as I could
To where it bent in the undergrowth;

Then took the other, as just as fair,
And having perhaps the better claim,
Because it was grassy and wanted wear;
Though as for that the passing there
Had worn them really about the same,

And both that morning equally lay
In leaves no step had trodden black.
Oh, I kept the first for another day!
Yet knowing how way leads on to way,
I doubted if I should ever come back.

I shall be telling this with a sigh
Somewhere ages and ages hence:
Two roads diverged in a wood, and I—
I took the one less travelled by,
And that has made all the difference.

LODGED

The rain to the wind said,
'You push and I'll pelt.'
They so smote the garden bed
That the flowers actually knelt,
And lay lodged—though not dead.
I know how the flowers felt.

NOTHING GOLD CAN STAY

Nature's first green is gold,
Her hardest hue to hold.
Her early leaf's a flower;
But only so an hour.
Then leaf subsides to leaf.
So Eden sank to grief,
So dawn goes down to day.
Nothing gold can stay.

BIRCHES

When I see birches bend to left and right
Across the lines of straighter darker trees,
I like to think some boy's been swinging on them.
But swinging doesn't bend them down to stay
As ice-storms do. Often you must have seen them
Loaded with ice a sunny winter morning
After a rain. They click upon themselves
As the breeze rises, and turn many-coloured
As the stir cracks and crazes their enamel.
Soon the sun's warmth makes them shed their crystal shells
Shattering and avalanching on the snow-crust—
Such heaps of broken glass to sweep away
You'd think the inner dome of heaven had fallen.
They are dragged to the withered bracken by the load,
And they seem not to break; though once they are bowed
So low for long, they never right themselves:
You may see their trunks arching in the woods
Years afterwards, trailing their leaves on the ground
Like girls on hands and knees that throw their hair
Before them over their heads to dry in the sun.
But I was going to say when Truth broke in
With all her matter-of-fact about the ice-storm
I should prefer to have some boy bend them
As he went out and in to fetch the cows—
Some boy too far from town to learn basketball,
Whose only play was what he found himself,
Summer or winter, and could play alone.
One by one he subdued his father's trees
By riding them down over and over again
Until he took the stiffness out of them,
And not one but hung limp, not one was left
For him to conquer. He learned all there was
To learn about not launching out too soon
And so not carrying the tree away
Clear to the ground. He always kept his poise
To the top branches, climbing carefully
With the same pains you use to fill a cup
Up to the brim, and even above the brim.
Then he flung outward, feet first, with a swish,
Kicking his way down through the air to the ground.
So was I once myself a swinger of birches.
And so I dream of going back to be.
It's when I'm weary of considerations,
And life is too much like a pathless wood
Where your face burns and tickles with the cobwebs
Broken across it, and one eye is weeping
From a twig's having lashed across it open.
I'd like to get away from earth awhile
And then come back to it and begin over.
May no fate wilfully misunderstand me
And half grant what I wish and snatch me away

Not to return. Earth's the right place for love:
I don't know where it's likely to go better.
I'd like to go by climbing a birch tree,
And climb black branches up a snow-white trunk
Toward heaven till the tree could bear no more,
But dipped its top and set me down again.
That would be good both going and coming back.
One could do worse than be a swinger of birches.

FIRE AND ICE

Some say the world will end in fire,
Some say in ice.
From what I've tasted of desire
I hold with those who favor fire.
But if it had to perish twice,
I think I know enough of hate
To say that for destruction ice
Is also great
And would suffice.

STOPPING BY WOODS ON A SNOWY EVENING

Whose woods these are I think I know.
His house is in the village, though;
He will not see me stopping here
To watch his woods fill up with snow.

My little horse must think it queer
To stop without a farmhouse near
Between the woods and frozen lake
The darkest evening of the year.

He gives his harness bells a shake
To ask if there is some mistake.
The only other sound's the sweep
Of easy wind and downy flake.

The woods are lovely, dark, and deep,
But I have promises to keep,
And miles to go before I sleep,
And miles to go before I sleep.

ACQUAINTED WITH THE NIGHT

I have been one acquainted with the night.
I have walked out in rain—and back in rain.
I have outwalked the furthest city light.

I have looked down the saddest city lane.
I have passed by the watchman on his beat
And dropped my eyes, unwilling to explain.

I have stood still and stopped the sound of feet
When far away an interrupted cry
Came over houses from another street,

But not to call me back or say good-by;
And further still at an unearthly height
One luminary clock against the sky

Proclaimed the time was neither wrong nor right.
I have been one acquainted with the night.

THE SILKEN TENT

She is as in a field a silken tent
At midday when a sunny summer breeze
Has dried the dew and all its ropes relent,
So that in guys it gently sways at ease,
And its supporting central cedar pole,
That is its pinnacle to heavenward
And signifies the sureness of the soul,
Seems to owe naught to any single cord,
But strictly held by none, is loosely bound
By countless silken ties of love and thought
To everything on earth the compass round,
And only by one's going slightly taut
In the capriciousness of summer air
Is of the slightest bondage made aware.

1922–1985

BORN IN COVENTRY WHERE his father, a Nazi sympathiser, was City Treasurer, and educated at King Henry VIII School, Larkin went to St John's College, Oxford and then became a librarian. He worked in a small town library and the university libraries of Leicester and Belfast before becoming chief librarian at Hull University. An only child, he had a love-hate relationship with his mother (whom he once described as 'that obsessive snivelling pest') yet to whom he wrote daily throughout her long life and with whom he shared many of his thoughts. His closeness to her and his own autumnal character are beautifully caught in 'Mother, Summer, I' (p. 182). Likewise his domineering and womanising father was someone whose approval he sought even though he was aware of his shortcomings. 'Days spent in black, twitching, boiling HATE!!!' he wrote of his childhood: yet still he sent his father poems.

Andrew Motion describes him as being a man of 'controlled but bitter resentment' in adult life. There is often a sense that somehow life has cheated him, that the country and the world are rapidly going down the drain as in 'Going Going' (p. 181), and that what should be fine and noble in life has become tawdry and cheapened – himself included. Many of his poems are shot through with guilt and with anger at feeling guilt. There is a sense of betrayal. How could other people achieve the knack of easy, natural relationships in life? Why could he not catch their happiness? And always in the back of his mind was the fear of the cancer which he had (accurately) predicted would kill him at the age of 63. There is an increasingly dark edge to his poetry. At 45 he described himself as 'periodically washed over by waves of sadness, remorse, fear and all the rest of it, like the automatic flushing of a urinal.'

It is out of such unpromising soil that some of the most influential poems of the twentieth century spring. As Alan Bennett remarks, 'it was only as a failure that Larkin could be a success.' Larkin is a sharp observer, and captures the small details of ordinary people's lives as in 'The Whitsun Weddings', (p. 178), where he finds his London-bound train picking up newly-married couples at almost every station. There is a mixture of unkindness and tenderness in his description of the 'grinning and pomaded girls / In parodies of fashion, heels and veils' and in his description of

> An uncle shouting smut; and then the perms,
> The nylon gloves and jewellery-substitutes,
> The lemons, mauves and olive-ochres that
> Marked off the girls unreally from the rest.

But there is perhaps a note of regret and envy in the last lines of the poem that, unlike these young couples whose lives together are just beginning, he is left an observer, sterile and alone.

Isolation is a recurring theme. The desperately lonely and unfulfilled figure of 'Mr. Bleaney' (p. 182), has more than a touch of Larkin himself in his character. The passing of time, the inevitability of change, of mortality, weighs heavily on him. The generations succeed each other remorselessly: even for the young mothers in the local park with their youngsters in his poem 'Afternoons'

> **Their beauty has thickened.**
> **Something is pushing them**
> **To the side of their own lives.**

What is the point of life he ponders in 'Ambulances', (p. 180), when we can 'sense the solving emptiness / That lies just under all we do.'? The inevitable end is death: 'All streets in time are visited' by the closed and quiet ambulances.

In his poem for the newborn Sally Amis, 'Born Yesterday', (p. 177), Larkin's wish for her is that she should be ordinary that, perhaps unlike himself, she should have

> **Nothing uncustomary**
> **To pull you off your balance,**
> **That unworkable itself,**
> **Stops all the rest from working.**

One can't help feeling that Larkin, 'pulled off balance' from earliest childhood, different, isolated, angry and fearful, who memorably did *not* write 'they tuck you up, your mum and dad,' knows what he is talking about.

OTHER POEMS

BORN YESTERDAY

for Sally Amis

Tightly-folded bud,
I have wished you something
None of the others would:
Not the usual stuff
About being beautiful,
Or running off a spring
Of innocence and love—
They will all wish you that,
And should it prove possible,
Well, you're a lucky girl.

But if it shouldn't, then
May you be ordinary;
Have, like other women,
An average of talents:

Not ugly, not good-looking,
Nothing uncustomary
To pull you off your balance,
That, unworkable itself,
Stops all the rest from working.
In fact, may you be dull—
If that is what a skilled,
Vigilant, flexible,
Unemphasised, enthralled
Catching of happiness is called.

THE WHITSUN WEDDINGS

That Whitsun, I was late getting away:
   Not till about
One-twenty on the sunlit Saturday
Did my three-quarters-empty train pull out,
All windows down, all cushions hot, all sense
Of being in a hurry gone. We ran
Behind the backs of houses, crossed a street
Of blinding windscreens, smelt the fish-dock; thence
The river's level drifting breadth began,
Where sky and Lincolnshire and water meet.

All afternoon, through the tall heat that slept
   For miles inland,
A slow and stopping curve southwards we kept.
Wide farms went by, short-shadowed cattle, and
Canals with floatings of industrial froth;
A hothouse flashed uniquely: hedges dipped
And rose: and now and then a smell of grass
Displaced the reek of buttoned carriage-cloth
Until the next town, new and nondescript,
Approached with acres of dismantled cars.

At first, I didn't notice what a noise
   The weddings made
Each station that we stopped at: sun destroys
The interest of what's happening in the shade,
And down the long cool platforms whoops and skirls
I took for porters larking with the mails,
And went on reading. Once we started, though,
We passed them, grinning and pomaded, girls
In parodies of fashion, heels and veils,
All posed irresolutely, watching us go,

As if out on the end of an event
   Waving goodbye
To something that survived it. Struck, I leant
More promptly out next time, more curiously,
And saw it all again in different terms:
The fathers with broad belts under their suits
And seamy foreheads; mothers loud and fat;
An uncle shouting smut; and then the perms,
The nylon gloves and jewellery-substitutes,
The lemons, mauves, and olive-ochres that

Marked off the girls unreally from the rest.
  Yes, from cafés
And banquet-halls up yards, and bunting-dressed
Coach-party annexes, the wedding-days
Were coming to an end. All down the line
Fresh couples climbed aboard: the rest stood round;
The last confetti and advice were thrown,
And, as we moved, each face seemed to define
Just what it saw departing: children frowned
At something dull; fathers had never known

Success so huge and wholly farcical;
  The women shared
The secret like a happy funeral;
While girls, gripping their handbags tighter, stared
At a religious wounding. Free at last,
And loaded with the sum of all they saw,
We hurried towards London, shuffling gouts of steam.
Now fields were building-plots, and poplars cast
Long shadows over major roads, and for
Some fifty minutes, that in time would seem

Just long enough to settle hats and say
  I nearly died,
A dozen marriages got under way.
They watched the landscape, sitting side by side
—An Odeon went past, a cooling tower,
And someone running up to bowl—and none
Thought of the others they would never meet
Or how their lives would all contain this hour.
I thought of London spread out in the sun,
Its postal districts packed like squares of wheat:

There we were aimed. And as we raced across
  Bright knots of rail
Past standing Pullmans, walls of blackened moss
Came close, and it was nearly done, this frail
Travelling coincidence; and what it held
Stood ready to be loosed with all the power
That being changed can give. We slowed again,
And as the tightened brakes took hold, there swelled
A sense of falling, like an arrow-shower
Sent out of sight, somewhere becoming rain.

AMBULANCES

Closed like confessionals, they thread
Loud noons of cities, giving back
None of the glances they absorb.
Light glossy grey, arms on a plaque,
They come to rest at any kerb:
All streets in time are visited.

Then children strewn on steps or road,
Or women coming from the shops
Past smells of different dinners, see
A wild white face that overtops
Red stretcher-blankets momently
As it is carried in and stowed,

And sense the solving emptiness
That lies just under all we do,
And for a second get it whole,
So permanent and blank and true.
The fastened doors recede. *Poor soul*,
They whisper at their own distress;

For borne away in deadened air
May go the sudden shut of loss
Round something nearly at an end,
And what cohered in it across
The years, the unique random blend
Of families and fashions, there

At last begin to loosen. Far
From the exchange of love to lie
Unreachable inside a room
The traffic parts to let go by
Brings closer what is left to come,
And dulls to distance all we are.

GOING, GOING

I thought it would last my time—
The sense that, beyond the town,
There would always be fields and farms,
Where the village louts could climb
Such trees as were not cut down;
I knew there'd be false alarms

In the papers about old streets
And split-level shopping, but some
Have always been left so far;
And when the old part retreats
As the bleak high-risers come
We can always escape in the car.

Things are tougher than we are, just
As earth will always respond
However we mess it about;
Chuck filth in the sea, if you must:
The tides will be clean beyond.
—But what do I feel now? Doubt?

Or age, simply? The crowd
Is young in the M1 café;
Their kids are screaming for more—
More houses, more parking allowed,
More caravan sites, more pay.
On the Business Page, a score

Of spectacled grins approve
Some takeover bid that entails
Five per cent profit (and ten
Per cent more in the estuaries): move
Your works to the unspoilt dales
(Grey area grants)! And when

You try to get near the sea
In summer . . .
            It seems, just now,
To be happening so very fast;
Despite all the land left free
For the first time I feel somehow
That it isn't going to last,

That before I snuff it, the whole
Boiling will be bricked in
Except for the tourist parts—
First slum of Europe: a role
It won't be so hard to win,
With a cast of crooks and tarts.

And that will be England gone,
The shadows, the meadows, the lanes,
The guildhalls, the carved choirs.
There'll be books; it will linger on
In galleries; but all that remains
For us will be concrete and tyres.

Most things are never meant.
This won't be, most likely: but
greeds
And garbage are too thick-
strewn
To be swept up now, or invent
Excuses that make them all
needs.
I just think it will happen, soon.

AFTERNOONS

Summer is fading:
The leaves fall in ones and twos
From trees bordering
The new recreation ground.
In the hollows of afternoons
Young mothers assemble
At swing and sandpit
Setting free their children.

Behind them, at intervals,
Stand husbands in skilled trades,
An estateful of washing,
And the albums, lettered
Our Wedding, lying
Near the television:
Before them, the wind
Is ruining their courting-places

That are still courting-places
(but the lovers are all in school),
And their children, so intent on
Finding more unripe acorns,
Expect to be taken home.
Their beauty has thickened.
Something is pushing them
To the side of their own lives.

MOTHER, SUMMER, I

My mother, who hates thunderstorms,
Holds up each summer day and shakes
It out suspiciously, lest swarms
Of grape-dark clouds are lurking there;
But when the August weather breaks
And rains begin, and brittle frost
Sharpens the bird-abandoned air,
Her worried summer look is lost.

And I her son, though summer-born
And summer-loving, none the less
Am easier when the leaves are gone;
Too often summer days appear
Emblems of perfect happiness
I can't confront: I must await
A time less bold, less rich, less clear:
An autumn more appropriate.

MR. BLEANEY

'This was Mr. Bleaney's room. He stayed
The whole time he was at the Bodies, till
They moved him.' Flowered curtains, thin and frayed,
Fall to within five inches of the sill,

Whose window shows a strip of building land,
Tussocky, littered. 'Mr. Bleaney took
My bit of garden properly in hand.'
Bed, upright chair, sixty-watt bulb, no hook

Behind the door, no room for books or bags—
'I'll take it.' So it happens that I lie
Where Mr. Bleaney lay, and stub my fags
On the same saucer-souvenir, and try

Stuffing my ears with cotton-wool, to drown
The jabbering set he egged her on to buy.
I know his habits—what time he came down,
His preference for sauce to gravy, why

He kept on plugging at the four aways—
Likewise their yearly frame: the Frinton folk
Who put him up for summer holidays,
And Christmas at his sister's house in Stoke.

But if he stood and watched the frigid wind
Tousling the clouds, lay on the fusty bed
Telling himself that this was home, and grinned,
And shivered, without shaking off the dread

That how we live measures our own nature,
And at his age having no more to show
Than one hired box should make him pretty sure
He warranted no better, I don't know.

SEAMUS HEANEY, THE ELDEST son of a family of eight children, was born on a farm in County Derry in Northern Ireland and grew up in a community where traditional methods of farming – horse ploughs, mowing with scythes, hand threshing – were still used. As a young boy, he saw many cattle-fairs in the Ulster countryside when he accompanied his father who was a cattle-dealer. The disappearance of this traditional way of life coincided with changes in his personal circumstances as his education in the 1950s and 1960s took him to Queen's University, Belfast as a student and then as a lecturer. Images of and reflections upon this rural upbringing are seen particularly in the first three poems of this selection (pp. 183–191).

The late 1960s also saw dramatic developments in the politics of Northern Ireland with the onset of the 'troubles' arising out of the protests by the catholic minority against economic and political discrimination. The violence by the 'provisional' wing of the IRA on one side and the Protestant Ulster Defence Association on the other led to the British government sending in troops in 1969, suspending the Ulster parliament in 1972, and assuming direct rule of the province in 1973.

At about this time Seamus Heaney left his academic post in Belfast to live in County Wicklow, in the Republic of Ireland, and to devote himself to full-time writing. For three years he made his living as a freelance writer, returning to Dublin in 1976. In 1984 he was appointed to a professorship at Harvard University and, in 1989, he became Professor of Poetry at Oxford University – two posts that have taken him away from Ireland for long periods but which have also given him time to pursue his own work. In 1995 he was awarded the Nobel Prize for Literature.

Over the years, the sectarian conflict has continued with much bloodshed on either side and only occasional periods of relative peace, such as occurred between the Summer of 1994 and February 1996 during the IRA's official ceasefire. Seamus Heaney has lived through this history and its imprint is marked, either metaphorically, as in the merging of poetry and politics in 'From the Frontier of Writing'; or symbolically, as in the so-called 'Bog poems' (pp. 188–191). Some background information about this last group is helpful.

Autobiographical memories of his early years, the historical archive of Irish history, and the more recent violence of the political struggle are all embedded in these poems. Seamus Heaney has written about the symbolism of the peat bog in an article called 'Feeling into Words' (*Selected Prose*, Faber) where he describes his reaction to photographs of some newly-discovered Iron Age bodies preserved in the peat bogs of Jutland in Denmark. Subsequently, he has introduced a reading of some of the poems on tape in the following way:

> 'I'd spent much time near bogs and mosses and so on when I was a youngster and, during the 1970s, all this pre-reflective familiarity with such places got crossed on other levels of awareness, first of all with an interest in archaeological finds that had been made in the bogs of Jutland – finds sometimes of the bodies of men and women, sometimes separately buried human limbs. I was terrifically entranced by these photographs because, terrible as they were, they were nevertheless riveting. And the theory that they had been part of some sacrificial ritual, . . . or part of some punishment for offences committed against the tribe, that made me think of them in relation to the whole ethos of self-sacrifice that had lain behind much twentieth century violence, whether in the so-to-speak official world war milieu or in national liberation movements like the IRA.'

Two of his earlier poems, 'Digging' and 'Bogland', show the importance of his memories of a rural upbringing and the sense of national history buried in the peat; the two 'bog poems', 'The Grauballe Man' and 'The Tollund Man', take the two most powerful of the bog bodies and use them as symbols of contemporary violence; and 'Tollund', Heaney tells us,

> '. . . was written after the IRA ceasefire of August 1994. The Sunday after that historic Wednesday I just happened to be for the first time in this bog in Jutland where they had found the body of the Tollund Man about whom I had written 24 years earlier. The mood of this more recent poem is as different from the earlier one as the dark mood of the early 70s in Ulster was from the more sanguine mid-90s.'

Try to hear Seamus Heaney reading and talking about his poetry on the cassette tape *Stepping Stones* (Penguin Audio Books, 1995), from which these extracts are taken.

OTHER POEMS

'Trout'   p. 129

DIGGING

Between my finger and my thumb
The squat pen rests; snug as a gun.

Under my window, a clean rasping sound
When the spade sinks into gravelly ground:
My father, digging. I look down

Till his straining rump among the flowerbeds
Bends low, comes up twenty years away
Stooping in rhythm through potato drills
Where he was digging.

The coarse boot nestled on the lug, the shaft
Against the inside knee was levered firmly.
He rooted out tall tops, buried the bright edge deep
To scatter new potatoes that we picked
Loving their cool hardness in our hands.

By God, the old man could handle a spade.
Just like his old man.

My grandfather cut more turf in a day
Than any other man on Toner's bog.
Once I carried him milk in a bottle
Corked sloppily with paper. He straightened up
To drink it, then fell to right away

Nicking and slicing neatly, heaving sods
Over his shoulder, going down and down
For the good turf. Digging.

The cold smell of potato mould, the squelch and slap
Of soggy peat, the curt cuts of an edge
Through living roots awaken in my head.
But I've no spade to follow men like them.

Between my finger and my thumb
The squat pen rests
I'll dig with it.

FOLLOWER

My father worked with a horse-plough,
His shoulders globed like a full sail strung
Between the shafts and the furrow.
The horses strained at his clicking tongue.

An expert. He would set the wing
And fit the bright steel-pointed sock.
The sod rolled over without breaking.
At the headrig, with a single pluck

Of reins, the sweating team turned round
And back into the land. His eye
Narrowed and angled at the ground,
Mapping the furrow exactly.

I stumbled in his hob-nailed wake,
Fell sometimes on the polished sod;
Sometimes he rode me on his back
Dipping and rising to his plod.

I wanted to grow up and plough,
To close one eye, stiffen my arm.
All I ever did was follow
In his broad shadow round the farm.

I was a nuisance, tripping, falling,
Yapping always. But today
It is my father who keeps stumbling
Behind me, and will not go away.

DEATH OF A NATURALIST

All year the flax-dam festered in the heart
Of the townland; green and heavy headed
Flax had rotted there, weighted down by huge sods.
Daily it sweltered in the punishing sun.
Bubbles gargled delicately, bluebottles
Wove a strong gauze of sound around the smell.
There were dragon-flies, spotted butterflies,
But best of all was the warm thick slobber
Of frogspawn that grew like clotted water
In the shade of the banks. Here, every spring
I would fill jampotfuls of the jellied
Specks to range on window-sills at home,
On shelves at school, and wait and watch until
The fattening dots burst into nimble-
Swimming tadpoles. Miss Walls would tell us how
The daddy frog was called a bullfrog
And how he croaked and how the mammy frog

Laid hundreds of little eggs and this was
Frogspawn. You could tell the weather by frogs too
For they were yellow in the sun and brown
In rain.

      Then one hot day when fields were rank
With cowdung in the grass the angry frogs
Invaded the flax-dam; I ducked through hedges
To a coarse croaking that I had not heard
Before. The air was thick with a bass chorus.
Right down the dam gross-bellied frogs were cocked
On sods; their loose necks pulsed like sails. Some hopped:
The slap and plop were obscene threats. Some sat
Poised like mud grenades, their blunt heads farting.
I sickened, turned, and ran. The great slime kings
Were gathered there for vengeance and I knew
That if I dipped my hand the spawn would clutch it.

FROM THE FRONTIER OF WRITING

The tightness and the nilness round that space
when the car stops in the road, the troops inspect
its make and number and, as one bends his face

towards your window, you catch sight of more
on a hill beyond, eyeing with intent
down cradled guns that hold you under cover

and everything is pure interrogation
until a rifle motions and you move
with guarded unconcerned acceleration—

a little emptier, a little spent
as always by that quiver in the self,
subjugated, yes, and obedient.

So you drive on to the frontier of writing
where it happens again. The guns on tripods;
the sergeant with his on–off mike repeating

data about you, waiting for the squawk
of clearance; the marksman training down
out of the sun upon you like a hawk.

And suddenly you're through, arraigned yet freed,
as if you'd passed from behind a waterfall
on the black current of a tarmac road

past armour-plated vehicles, out between
the posted soldiers flowing and receding
like tree shadows into the polished windscreen.

BOGLAND

We have no prairies
To slice a big sun at evening—
Everywhere the eye concedes to
Encroaching horizon,

Is wooed into the cyclops' eye
Of a tarn. Our unfenced country
Is bog that keeps crusting
Between the sights of the sun.

They've taken the skeleton
Of the great Irish Elk
Out of the peat, set it up
An astounding crate full of air.

Butter sunk under
More than a hundred years
Was recovered salty and white.
The ground itself is kind, black butter

Melting and opening underfoot,
Missing its last definition
By millions of years.
They'll never dig coal here,

Only the waterlogged trunks
Of great firs, soft as pulp.
Our pioneers keep striking
Inwards and downwards,

Every layer they strip
Seems camped on before.
The bogholes might be Atlantic seepage.
The wet centre is bottomless.

THE GRAUBALLE MAN

As if he had been poured
in tar, he lies
on a pillow of turf
and seems to weep

the black river of himself.
The grain of his wrists
is like bog oak,
the ball of his heel

like a basalt egg.
His instep has shrunk
cold as a swan's foot
or a wet swamp root.

His hips are the ridge
and purse of a mussel,
his spine an eel arrested
under a glisten of mud.

The head lifts,
the chin is a visor
raised above the vent
of his slashed throat

that has tanned and
toughened.
The cured wound
opens inwards to a dark
elderberry place.

Who will say 'corpse'
to his vivid cast?
Who will say 'body'
to his opaque repose?

And his rusted hair,
a mat unlikely
as a foetus's.
I first saw his twisted face

in a photograph,
a head and shoulder
out of the peat,
bruised like a forceps baby,

but now he lies
perfected in my memory,
down to the red horn
of his nails,

hung in the scales
with beauty and atrocity:
with the Dying Gaul
too strictly compassed

on his shield,
with the actual weight
of each hooded victim,
slashed and dumped.

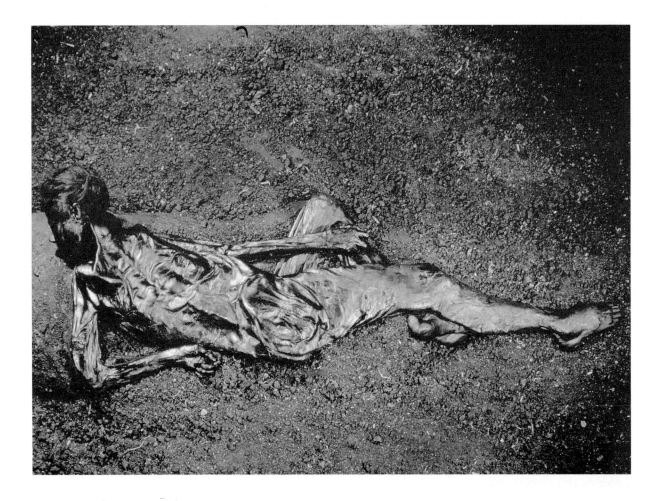

THE TOLLUND MAN

I
Some day I will go to Aarhus
To see his peat-brown head,
The mild pods of his eye-lids,
His pointed skin cap.

In the flat country nearby
Where they dug him out,
His last gruel of winter seeds
Caked in his stomach,

Naked except for
The cap, noose and girdle,
I will stand a long time.
Bridegroom to the goddess,

She tightened her torc on him
And opened her fen,
Those dark juices working
Him to a saint's kept body,

Trove of the turfcutters'
Honeycombed workings.
Now his stained face
Reposes at Aarhus.

II
I could risk blasphemy,
Consecrate the cauldron bog
Our holy ground and pray
Him to make germinate

The scattered, ambushed
Flesh of labourers,
Stockinged corpses
Laid out in the farmyards,

Tell-tale skin and teeth
Flecking the sleepers
Of four young brothers, trailed
For miles along the lines.

III
Something of his sad freedom
As he rode the tumbril
Should come to me, driving,
Saying the names

Tollund, Grauballe, Nebelgard,
Watching the pointing hands
Of country people,
Not knowing their tongue.

Out there in Jutland
In the old man-killing parishes
I will feel lost,
Unhappy and at home.

TOLLUND

That Sunday morning we had travelled far.
We stood a long time out in Tollund Moss:
The low ground, the swart water, the thick grass
Hallucinatory and familiar.

A path through Jutland fields. Light traffic sound.
Willow bushes; rushes; bog-fir grags
In a swept and gated farmyard; dormant quags.
And silage under wraps in its silent mound.

It could have been a still out of the bright
'Townland of Peace', that poem of dream farms
Outside all contention. The scarecrow's arms
Stood open opposite the satellite

Dish in the paddock, where a standing stone
Had been resituated and landscaped,
With tourist signs in *futhark* runic script
In Danish and in English. Things had moved on.

It could have been Mulhollandstown or Scribe.
The byroads had their names on them in black
And white; it was user-friendly outback
Where we stood footloose, at home beyond the tribe,

More scouts than strangers, ghosts who'd walked abroad
Unfazed by light, to make a new beginning
And make a go of it, alive and sinning,
Ourselves again, free-willed again, not bad.

GILLIAN CLARKE WAS BORN in Cardiff and educated at the University there. After a short time working for the BBC in London, she returned to Wales in 1960, and has lived and worked there ever since. She published her first poems in the 1970s and her work became more widely known with *Letter From a Far Country* (1982). The long title poem was commissioned by the BBC as a half-hour radio poem and takes the form of a letter from a fictitious woman to men in general. It is both a feminist protest and a celebration of the rich details of local Welsh life.

Many of Gillian Clarke's poems combine a sense of the contribution women make to society with a clear eye for personal, domestic details and for the relationships within families and between friends (e.g. 'Still Life'). The tone may be reflective ('The Sundial') or bitter-sweet ('Overheard in County Sligo'); the occasion may be a poetry reading ('Miracle on St David's Day'), or the effects of the Chernobyl disaster in 1986 ('Neighbours'). In all these poems she relates local details to a more general awareness of the values by which people live.

GILLIAN Clarke

STILL LIFE

It was good tonight
To polish brass with you,
Our hands slightly gritty
With Brasso, as they would feel
If we'd been in the sea, salty.
It was as if we burnished
Our friendship, polished it
Until all the light-drowning
Tarnish of deceit
Were stroked away. Patterns
Of incredible honesty
Delicately grew, revealed
Quite openly to the pressure
Of the soft, torn rag.
We made a yellow-gold
Still-life out of clocks,
Candlesticks and kettles.
My sadness puzzled you.
I rubbed the full curve
Of an Indian goblet,
Feeling its illusory
Heat. It cooled beneath
My fingers and I read
In the braille formality
Of pattern, in the leaf
And tendril and stylised tree,
That essentially each
Object remains cold,
Separate, only reflecting
The other's warmth.

THE SUNDIAL

Owain was ill today. In the night
He was delirious, shouting of lions
In the sleepless heat. Today, dry
And pale, he took a paper circle,
Laid it on the grass which held it
With curling fingers. In the still
Centre he pushed the broken bean
Stick, gathering twelve fragments
Of stone, placed them at measured
Distances. Then he crouched, slightly
Trembling with fever, calculating
The mathematics of sunshine.

He looked up, his eyes dark,
Intelligently adult as though
The wave of fever taught silence
And immobility for the first time.
Here, in his enforced rest, he found
Deliberation, and the slow finger
Of light, quieter than night lions,
More worthy of his concentration.
All day he told the time to me.
All day we felt and watched the sun
Caged in its white diurnal heat,
Pointing at us with its black stick.

OVERHEARD IN COUNTY SLIGO

I married a man from County Roscommon
and I live at the back of beyond
with a field of cows and a yard of hens
and six white geese on the pond.

At my door's a square of yellow corn
caught up by its corners and shaken,
and the road runs down through the open gate
and freedom's there for the taking.

I had thought to work on the Abbey stage
or have my name in a book,
to see my thought on the printed page,
or still the crowd with a look.

But I turn to fold the breakfast cloth
and to polish the lustre and brass,
to order and dust the tumbled rooms
and find my face in the glass.

I ought to feel I'm a happy woman
for I lie in the lap of the land,
and I married a man from County Roscommon
and I live in the back of beyond.

NO HANDS

War-planes have been at it all day long
shaking the world, strung air
humming like pianos when children bang the keys

over and over; willow warbler song
and jet planes; lads high on speed up there
in a mindless thrum; down here a brake of trees

churns to a rolling wave and there's no let
in the after-quiver along air-waves struck
by silly boys who think they strum guitars,

who skim the fields like surfboards over crests
of hedges, where a tractor swims in a green wake
of grass dust tossed to dry under sun and stars:

boy scaring boy off the face of his own land,
all do and dare, and look at me, no hands.

MIRACLE ON ST DAVID'S DAY

They flash upon that inward eye
Which is the bliss of solitude
'The Daffodils' by W. Wordsworth

An afternoon yellow and open-mouthed
with daffodils. The sun treads the path
among cedars and enormous oaks.
It might be a country house, guests strolling,
the rumps of gardeners between nursery shrubs.

I am reading poetry to the insane.
An old woman, interrupting, offers
as many buckets of coal as I need.
A beautiful chestnut-haired boy listens
entirely absorbed. A schizophrenic

on a good day, they tell me later.
In a cage of first March sun a woman
sits not listening, not seeing, not feeling.
In her neat clothes the woman is absent.
A big, mild man is tenderly led

to his chair. He has never spoken.
His labourer's hands on his knees, he rocks
gently to the rhythms of the poems.
I read to their presences, absences,
to the big, dumb labouring man as he rocks.

He is suddenly standing, silently,
huge and mild, but I feel afraid. Like slow
movement of spring water or the first bird
of the year in the breaking darkness,
the labourer's voice recites 'The Daffodils'.

The nurses are frozen, alert; the patients
seem to listen. He is hoarse but word-perfect.
Outside the daffodils are still as wax,
a thousand, ten thousand, their syllables
unspoken, their creams and yellows still.

Forty years ago, in a Valleys school,
the class recited poetry by rote.
Since the dumbness of misery fell
he has remembered there was a music
of speech and that once he had something to say.

When he's done, before the applause, we observe
the flowers' silence. A thrush sings
And the daffodils are flame.

NEIGHBOURS

That spring was late. We watched the sky
and studied charts for shouldering isobars.
Birds were late to pair. Crows drank from the lamb's eye.

Over Finland small birds fell: song-thrushes
steering north, smudged signatures on light,
migrating warblers, nightingales.

Wing-beats failed over fjords, each lung a sip of gall.
Children were warned of their dangerous beauty.
Milk was spilt in Poland. Each quarrel

the blowback from some old story,
a mouthful of bitter air from the Ukraine
brought by the wind out of its box of sorrows.

This spring a lamb sips caesium on a Welsh hill.
A child, lifting her face to drink the rain,
takes into her blood the poisoned arrow.

Now we are all neighbourly, each little town
in Europe twinned to Chernobyl, each heart
with the burnt fireman, the child on the Moscow train.

In the democracy of the virus and the toxin
we wait. We watch for bird migrations,
one bird returning with green in its voice,

glasnost,
golau glas,★
a first break of blue.

★blue light

BORDER

It crumbles
where the land forgets its name
and I'm foreign in my own country.
Fallow, pasture, ploughland
ripped from the hill
beside a broken farm.

The word's exactness
slips from children's tongues.
Saints fade in the parishes.
Fields blur between the scar
of hedgerow and new road.
History forgets itself.

At the garage they're polite.
'Sorry love, no Welsh.'
At the shop I am slapped
by her hard 'What!'
They came for the beauty
but could not hear it speak.

CHIP-HOG

Hog-of-the-road,
leaf-scuffer,
little tramp of the lanes

—like the old bearded one
wheel-wobbling his bicycle
weighed to the saddle
with string bags, ropes,
a rosary of tin mugs,
or hunkered down for the winter
under threadbare thatch.

Pin-cushion,
boot-brush,
flea-bag,
eye-in-the-leafpile.

One fifth of November,
we lifted him just in time,
safe on a shovel from the smoke
of his smouldering house
his spines sparking like stars.

Milk-scrounger,
slug-scavenger,
haunter of back doors and bins.

Once, kissing goodnight at the gate,
we saw a ghost:
something white, something small, something scratching,
headlong, hellbent, heel-over-tip hedgehog,
head in a chip-bag and hooked
on his own prickles,
the last chip escaping him
as fast as he could run.

born 1947

LIZ LOCHHEAD WAS BORN in Motherwell, Scotland. She started to write poetry when she was an Art student in Glasgow in the 1960s and continued to do so while working as an Art teacher for eight years. Many of the poems from her early books are included in *Dreaming Frankenstein and Collected Poems*, (Polygon Books, 1984). She published a collection of song lyrics, performance pieces, raps and monologues in *True Confessions and New Cliches* (Polygon Books, 1985) and an equally varied book of poetry and prose called *Bagpipe Muzak* (Penguin, 1991). She is a playwright and has also written for television and radio.

Liz Lochhead's poems are full of characters, but they are never merely pictures of people in words; her characters are portraits with a point. This selection begins with a poem about gender ('Mo'), which shows the wry sense of humour that appears in much of Liz Lochhead's writing. If her poems make the reader smile, then it's usually a thoughtful smile, as in 'Kidspoem/Bairnsang'. 'The Choosing' and 'Poem for my Sister' read like reports of real incidents, or, at least, significant scenes created from a basis in actual experience. Others, by contrast, deal with the ways in which traditional stories create their fictional characters and events: the 'storyteller poems' (p. 204), are about the conventional images of people in folk and fairy tales. Above all, Liz Lochhead's poems gain from being read aloud: their humour, conversational idiom and informal rhythms lend themselves to performance.

OTHER POEMS

MO

Men says My Boss
are definitely more dependable
and though even in these days of equal pay
men tend to come a wee bitty more expensive
due to the added responsibility a man tends to have
in his jobspecification
Well for instance you can depend on a man not to get pregnant.
My Boss says men are more objective.
Catch a man bitching
about healthhazards and conditions
and going out on strike over no papertowels in the toilet
or nagging over the lack of day nursery facilities
My Boss says as far as he's concerned a crêche is a motor accident in Kelvinside★
and any self respecting woman should have a good man
to take care of her so its only pinmoney anyway
and that's bound to come out in the attitude.
Well a man isn't subject to moods
or premenstrual tension a guy
isn't going to phone in sick with some crap about cramps.
My Boss says a man rings in
with an upset stomach and you know either
he means a hangover or else his brother
managed to get him a ticket for Wembley.

You know where you are with a man.

★ *Kelvinside: a respectable district in Glasgow, whose inhabitants reputedly speak with an exaggeratedly 'refined' accent.*

THE CHOOSING

We were first equal Mary and I
with the same coloured ribbons in mouse-coloured hair,
and with equal shyness
we curtseyed to the lady councillor
for copies of Collins' Children's Classics.
First equal, equally proud.

Best friends too Mary and I
a common bond in being cleverest (equal)
in our small school's small class.
I remember
the competition for top desk
or to read aloud the lesson
at school service.
And my terrible fear
of her superiority at sums.

I remember the housing scheme
where we both stayed.
The same house, different homes,
where the choices were made.

I don't know exactly why they moved,
but anyway they went.
Something about a three-apartment
and a cheaper rent.
But from the top deck of the high-school bus
I'd glimpse among the others on the corner
Mary's father, mufflered, contrasting strangely
with the elegant greyhounds by his side.
He didn't believe in high-school education,
especially for girls,
or in forking out for uniforms.

Ten years later on a Saturday—
I am coming home from the library—
sitting near me on the bus,
Mary
with a husband who is tall,
curly haired, has eyes
for no one else but Mary.
Her arms are round the full-shaped vase
that is her body.
Oh, you can see where the attraction lies
in Mary's life—
not that I envy her, really.

And I am coming from the library
with my arms full of books.
I think of the prizes that were ours for the taking
and wonder when the choices got made
we don't remember making.

POEM FOR MY SISTER

My little sister likes to try my shoes,
to strut in them,
admire her spindle-thin twelve-year-old legs
in this season's styles.
She says they fit her perfectly,
but wobbles
on their high heels, they're
hard to balance.

I like to watch my little sister
playing hopscotch, admire the neat hops-and-skips of her,
their quick peck,
never-missing their mark, not
over-stepping the line.
She is competent at peever*.   * *hopscotch*

I try to warn my little sister
about unsuitable shoes,
point out my own distorted feet, the calluses,
odd patches of hard skin.
I should not like to see her
in my shoes.
I wish she could stay
sure footed,
            sensibly shod.

THE FATHER

loving and bungling,
offending the evil fairy by forgetting
her invitation to the Christening,
or being tricked into bartering his beloved daughter
in exchange for the rose he only
took to please her—
then compounding it all
by over-protectiveness and suppression
(banning
spinning wheels indeed
when the sensible thing would have been
to familiarize her from the cradle
and explain their power to hurt her).

But when she comes,
the beautiful daughter,
leading her lover by the sleeve, laughing—
'Come and meet my daddy, the King,
he's absolutely a hundred years behind the times
but such a dear.'
and she's (note Redeeming Kiss)
wide-eyed and aware.
Stirring, forgiven, full of love and terror,
her father hears her footstep on the stair.

THE MOTHER

is always two-faced.
At best, she wished you
into being. Yes, it was she
cried at the seven drops of blood that fell,
staining the snow—she
who bargained crazily with Fate
for that longawaited child
as red as blood
as white as snow
and when you came true it was
she who clapped her hands merrily because
she was as happy as a Queen could be.
But she's always dying early,
so often it begins to look deliberate,
abandoning you,
leaving you to the terrible mercy
of the Worst Mother, the one who married your father.
She doesn't like you, she
prefers all your sisters, she
loves her sons.
She's jealous of mirrors.
She wants your heart in a casket.
When she cuts the apple in two and selflessly
takes the sour green half
she's good and glad to see you poisoned
by the sweet red pulp.
Tell me,
what kind of prudent parent
would send a little child on a foolish errand in the forest
with a basket jammed with goodies
and wolf-bait? Don't trust her an inch.

STORYTELLER

she sat down
at the scoured table
in the swept kitchen
beside the dresser with its cracked delft.
And every last crumb of daylight was salted away.

No one could say the stories were useless
for as the tongue clacked
five or forty fingers stitched
corn was grated from the husk
patchwork was pieced
or the darning done.

Never the one to slander her shiftless.
Daily sloven or spotless no matter whether
dishwater or tasty was her soup.
To tell the stories was her work.
It was like spinning,
gathering thin air to the singlest strongest
thread. Night in
she'd have us waiting, held
breath, for the ending we knew by heart.

And at first light
as women stirred themselves to build the fire
as the peasant's feet felt for clogs
as thin grey washed over flat fields
the stories dissolved in the whorl of the ear
but they
hung themselves upside down
in the sleeping heads of the children
till they flew again
in the storytellers night.

RAPUNZSTILTSKIN

& just when our maiden had got
good & used to her isolation,
stopped daily expecting to be rescued,
had come to almost love her tower,
along comes This Prince
with absolutely
all the wrong answers.
Of course she had not been brought up to look for
originality or gingerbread
so at first she was quite undaunted
by his tendency to talk in strung-together cliché.
'Just hang on and we'll get you out of there'
he hollered like a fireman in some soap opera
when she confided her plight (the old
hag inside etc. & how trapped she was);
well, it was corny but
he did look sort of gorgeous
axe and all.
So there she was, humming & pulling
all the pins out of her chignon,
throwing him all the usual lifelines
till, soon, he was shimmying in & out
every other day as though
he owned the place, bringing her
the sex manuals & skeins of silk
from which she was meant, eventually,
to weave the means of her own escape.
'All very well & good,' she prompted,
'but when exactly?'
She gave him till
well past the bell on the timeclock.
She mouthed at him, hinted,
she was keener than a T.V. quizmaster
that he should get it right.
'I'll do everything in my power' he intoned, 'but
the impossible (she groaned) might
take a little longer.' He grinned.
She pulled her glasses off.
'All the better
to see you with my dear?' he hazarded.
She screamed, cut off her hair.
'Why, you're beautiful?' he guessed tentatively.
'No, No, No!' she
shrieked & stamped her foot so
hard it sank six cubits through the floorboards.
'I love you?' he came up with
as finally she tore herself in two.

KIDSPOEM/BAIRNSANG

It wis January
and a gey dreich day
the first day I went to the school
so
ma Mum happed me up in ma good navyblue nap coat
wi the rid tartan hood
birled a scarf aroon ma neck
pu'ed on ma pixie and ma pawkies
it wis that bitter
said
'noo ye'll no starve'
gied me a wee kiss and a kidoan skelp on the bum
and sent me off across the playground
to the place I'd learn to say
'It was January
and a really dismal day
the first day I went to school
so
my Mother wrapped me up in my best navyblue top coat
with the red tartan hood
twirled a scarf around my neck
pulled on my bobble-hat and mittens
it was so bitterly cold
said
"now you won't freeze to death"
gave me a little kiss and a pretend slap on the bottom
and sent me off across the playground
to the place I'd learn to forget to say
"It wis January
and a gey dreich day
the first day I went to the school
so
ma Mum happed me up in ma good navyblue nap coat
wi the rid tartan hood
birled a scarf aroon ma neck
pu'ed on ma pixie and ma pawkies
it wis that bitter." '

Oh,
saying it was one thing
but when it came to writing it
in black and white
the way it had to be said
was as if
you were grown up, posh, male, English and dead.

Ten Poets
WORKSHOP

---

1 POETRY PROGRAMME 'MEET THE POET'

Television and radio often have short poetry programmes in a variety of formats. These feature the annual National Poetry Day, readings of the nation's favourite poems, celebrities choosing poems that they like, BBC Radio 4's *Poetry Please* series, and so on. The task here is along similar lines.

In groups (10 groups, one per poet)

● Prepare a short (5–10 minutes) programme for radio or TV to introduce the work of one of these ten poets to the rest of the class. Your programme should say what your group thinks of the poems and include:
 — some introductory comments, relevant background details and, perhaps, one or two quotations from the poems that, *for you*, best sum up the poet's work.
 — linked readings of four or five poems. You will need to agree your choices, decide the order of the poems and whose voices you are going to use. Prepare some brief connecting comments to link the readings.
 — a summary of, say, three or four main points that you notice about the writer.

When you have rehearsed your readings and scripted your links, present your programme either live or taped.

---

2 PORTFOLIO ON A POET

The aim here is to compile a portfolio of coursework on *one* of these ten poets.

On your own

● Your portfolio should include the following items and any other information or pieces of writing that help to fill out the picture of the poet's work.
 — a cover design which captures the main themes of your chosen poet;
 — a contents list of the items in your portfolio;
 — a collection of favourite lines and phrases, with a note to say what you like about each;
 — an open letter to the poet, saying which poems you like and why, and raising any questions you might have. (These can be followed up in class discussion);
 — your favourite poem with your own responses to it 'mapped' in note form around the text. You will need to copy out the poem carefully in the centre of a page and then, with a pen of a different colour, make your notes. Underneath, complete the single sentence: 'I like this poem because . . .'.

— a pastiche poem of your own; that is, one written in the same style as that of your chosen poet.

— an essay describing what you think are the main qualities of your chosen poet. Comment on the subjects the writer deals with and the language, forms, feelings and ideas that you notice in the poems you discuss.

Remember to look up any other poems by the poet you choose in Parts A and B of this book; they are listed on the introductory page for each writer. Below are some further writing suggestions and some references you may be able to follow up in the library.

Shakespeare: *The Sonnets*, ed. R. Gibson, Cambridge University Press.
● Include two or three passages from any of Shakespeare's plays which you have read and say why you like them.

Blake: *The Songs of Innocence and Experience*, ed. Sir G. Keynes, Oxford.
● Include copies of one or two of Blake's illustrations to his poems from this illuminated edition of his work, and/or draw your own illustration to interpret one of Blake's poems.

Wordsworth: *Selected Poetry*, ed. N. Roe, Penguin.
● Wordsworth is a poet of landscape, particularly that of the Lake District. Find some photographs of this region that you can copy which capture the mood and atmosphere of the poems. The Wordsworth Trust, Dove Cottage, Grasmere, Cumbria, LA22 9SH may also provide you with useful information.

Rossetti: *Christina Rossetti*, ed. Jan Marsh, Everyman, Dent.
● Find out more about the two people referred to in the poem, 'In an Artist's Studio' (p. 161) – her brother, Dante Gabriel Rossetti and Elizabeth Siddal, his model and later his wife. The following books will help you: *Rossetti* by David Rodgers, Phaidon; *Elizabeth Siddal, 1829–1862, Pre-Raphaelite Artist*, by Jan Marsh.

Hardy: *Selected Shorter Poems*, ed. J. Wain, Macmillan.
● Hardy is as well known for his fiction as for his poetry; and all his writing reflects his Dorset background and the wider area he called Wessex. Include some copies of photographs of the Dorset landscape to accompany the poems. Try to extend your portfolio with one or two extracts from any of Hardy's novels or short stories that you know.

Frost: *Selected Poems*, ed. I. Hamilton, Penguin.
● One of Robert Frost's great strengths is to reflect on simple, everyday objects and to 'tell the story' of their importance to him. Try to do the same. Focus upon some particular memory or object, perhaps from early childhood, and write your own poem to include in your portfolio.

Larkin: *Collected Poems*, ed. A. Thwaite, Marvell/Faber.
● Larkin was a person who only rarely gave interviews and left few recordings of his poetry readings. A most useful insight into his work is in the Penguin Audiobooks, *Whitsun Weddings* and *High Windows*, two cassette tapes of Alan Bennett's readings of Larkin's verse.

Heaney: *Selected Poems 1966–87*, Faber.
● Two aspects of Heaney's work that are intertwined are his background in rural Ireland and his experience of the 'troubles'—the political and cultural divide, which erupts continuously into violence, between the Protestants and the Catholics. Find out more about the political background (see, for example, *The Course of Irish History*, ed. T.W. Moody and F.X. Martin); and include copies of one or two newspaper photographs of Northern Ireland which, for you, convey the sense of the 'troubles'.

Clarke: *Selected Poems*, Carcanet.

● Gillian Clarke's Welsh background pervades all her writing. You could extend your portfolio by reading her radio-poem *Letter from a Far Country* (details on her introductory page) and incorporating some quotations and your own comments.

Lochhead: *Dreaming Frankenstein and Collected Poems*, Polygon Books.

● Liz Lochhead's sequence of poems about fairy and folk tales (pp. 203–204) is one that could be easily extended. Read them again, especially 'Rapunzstiltskin', and write your own modern version of a fairy tale along similar lines; Cinderella, Snow White, Little Red Riding Hood are all waiting.

3 TOPIC FOLDER

On your own/in pairs

Compile a folder of coursework on *one* of the following topics or, in discussion with your teacher, devise your own.

(i) A sense of place

Some poems paint particular scenes from remembered childhoods such as Wordsworth stealing a boat on Lake Windermere ('Stealing a Boat', p. 154), or Heaney's remembering his earlier boyhood habit of collecting frogspawn ('Death of a Naturalist', p. 186). Others use places to focus a feeling or an idea—Robert Frost is especially skilled at suggesting the ghosts of other thoughts and emotions associated with apparently simple descriptions of a snowy landscape ('Stopping by Woods on a Snowy Evening', p. 174), city streets ('Acquainted with the Night', p. 175), or country lanes ('The Road Not Taken', p. 172).

Or, again, some places are symbolic such as in 'Up-Hill' (p. 161), 'Border' (p. 196), or 'Tollund' (p. 191); whereas others are literal descriptions such as Wordsworth's 'Upon Westminster Bridge' (p. 156).

● Make a mini-anthology of, say, six poems which are all rooted in a sense of place. Write a paragraph on each poem saying what place is being described and how the poet has used it to convey a feeling, or an idea, or an atmosphere. Introduce your folder with a short essay which explains the reasons for your choices and comments on any general points about poems of place that you have noticed.

(ii) Aspects of love

Many of the love poems here are by men writing to their real or imagined lovers: Shakespeare's 'Sonnets' (p. 146), Wordworth's two 'Lucy' poems, (p. 158), and Hardy's sequence of poems (pp. 166–167), are all variations on this theme. But there are other aspects of love that the poems explore:

— Blake's 'The Garden of Love' (p. 150) and 'Song' (p. 148) both, in different ways, suggest the losses and constraints which accompany love and restrict its freedom of expression;

— Larkin (pp. 178–179) and Clarke (p. 194) both write about married love but at different stages and with very different feelings.

— Rossetti writes about her brother's obsessive love for a woman he paints over and over again (p. 161);

● As above, make a mini-anthology of, say, six love poems drawn either from the suggestions here or from the collection in Part B of this book (pp. 87–92). Write an Introduction to your folder explaining your choices and write a paragraph about each poem saying what aspect of love it deals with and what appeals to you about the poet's approach to the topic.

(iii) Telling stories

Some narrative poems arise out of apparently real incidents, for example, 'Miracle on St. David's Day' (p. 195), or 'The Choosing' (p. 200); others are dramatic accounts of, or reflections on, public events like the Battle of Agincourt (p. 142) or the sinking of the Titanic (p. 170).

Some stories seem to withhold their point, ('Winter: My Secret' p. 164); others all but poke you in the eye with theirs, (Hardy's 'In Church' p. 168).

Shakespeare's 'All the World's a Stage' (p. 144) gives everyman his life story in a conventional series of seven images; whereas, Lochhead's 'fairytale' poems (pp. 203–204) challenge the stereotypes of traditional stories.

● Three aspects of storytelling: (i) significant events or moments of truth, either on a personal or national scale; (ii) stories with a sharp point to make about human behaviour; and, (iii) characterisation – how images of people are constructed in stories.

— Choose one of these themes and select, say, six poems which illustrate it. For each poem you include, first, summarise the story being told and, then, write about how the poet puts the story or incident across to the reader, the attitude he or she takes, and the purpose in telling it.

— Below, we have given a working title for each theme and a list of six poems you might consider; but, you may come up with a different list by including one or two choices from elsewhere in the book and you may think of a more appropriate title for your theme.

(i) *Moments of Truth:*	'Miracle on St. David's Day'	p. 195
	'The Choosing'	p. 200
	'Before Agincourt'	p. 142
	'The Convergence of the Twain'	p. 170
	'From the Frontier of Writing'	p. 187
	'Stealing a Boat'	p. 154
(ii) *Pointed Stories:*	'In Church'	p. 168
	'A Poison Tree'	p. 151
	'Mo'	p. 199
	'The Ruined Maid'	p. 168
	'Fire and Ice'	p. 174
	'Going, Going'	p. 181
(iii) *Character Sketches:*	'Winter: My Secret'	p. 164
	'The Father'	p. 201
	'The Mother'	p. 202
	'Follower'	p. 186
	'Mr. Bleaney'	p. 182
	'Mother, Summer, I'	p. 182

Glossary
OF TECHNICAL TERMS

There are scores of technical terms to describe different poetic structures and techniques: fortunately, it is perfectly possible to talk intelligently and sensitively about poetry using very few of them. Nonetheless, we have found it helpful to use several of them once or twice at least in the course of this book and have listed those that appear in the text along with a few others that you are likely to come across and that you may yourself find it helpful to use as you gain more confidence in talking and writing about poetry.

alliteration (note the spelling: NOT **ill ...!**) When the same consonant sound is repeated in words or syllables in close succession. It usually refers to the repetition of a sound or letter at the beginning of words, as in

> He clasps the crag with hooked hands

where the repetition of the *c* and *h* helps the sound to echo the meaning when we say the line aloud, but it can appear elsewhere in the line as in

> Fields ever fresh and groves ever green

where, apart from the repetition of *f* and *g* there is a less noticeable repetition of the letter *v*. In this book, 'Esther's Tomcat' on p. 121 offers many examples.

assonance The echoing of similar vowel sounds in the same line or consecutive lines. Thus *place* and *fade* are assonance.

ballad A narrative poem (i.e. one that tells a story) usually written in four line stanzas rhyming *abcb* or *abab*. It may have a repeated refrain (i.e. a line or verse that is repeated at certain fixed points in the poem). The language is usually simple.

blank verse Verse composed of an indefinite number of unrhymed iambic pentameters. Most of Shakespeare's plays, for example the passages from *Henry V* and *As You Like It* (pp. 142–144), and much of Wordsworth's poetry are in blank verse. The passages from *The Prelude* on pp. 154–155 are examples of blank verse from Wordsworth. (See **iambic pentameter** under **rhythm, stress, metre** below.)

consonant A speech sound which is not a vowel, for example b, c, d, f, g, h, j are consonants. Consonants are combined with a vowel to make a syllable. (See **vowel**.)

couplet A pair of lines usually of the same metre which have a common rhyme, as in

> **True ease in writing comes from art, not chance,**
> **As those move easiest who have learned to dance.**

Further examples will be found on pp. 22–23.

free verse Poetry which has no regular metre or rhyme pattern as, for example, 'Snake' on p. 126. Properly, the content and mood of the poem suggest its form or shape on the page.

haiku A form of tightly structured formal Japanese poem which in its English form, usually has seventeen syllables arranged in three lines of five, seven and five syllables. This 'rule' is often broken in translations of haiku into English where stress rather than syllable counting is more important.

image/imagery Images in poetry are pictures or sense impressions conveyed in words by the writer. An image in poetry is one which has a direct appeal to one or more of our five senses and will often involve a comparison between two or more usually unrelated objects (see **simile** and **metaphor**). One can talk about the images George Herbert uses in 'The Church-Floore' (p. 11) or about George Herbert's imagery.

irony/ironic Irony is when a writer suggests a meaning which might be quite different from, even opposite to, the one he or she *appears* to offer us. We may sometimes say something is ironic when the opposite of what we might have expected actually happens and causes a certain amount of amusement.

metaphor A direct comparison of one thing with another without the introductory *like* or *as*. Sylvia Plath's poem 'Metaphors' on p. 37 is a series of such direct comparisons. Describing her pregnancy she writes she is 'An elephant, a ponderous house / A melon strolling on two tendrils'; she does not write that she is *like* an elephant, etc. The poem 'Behaviour of Fish in an Egyptian Tea Garden' on p. 9 also uses several metaphors. Such comparison is at the heart of poetry and like simile it yokes together in words, and so in the images in our minds, things we had not previously connected. Louis Untermeyer wrote: 'Its element is surprise. To relate the hitherto un-related, to make the strange seem familiar and the familiar seem strange is the aim of metaphor. Through this heightened awareness, poetry, though variously defined, is invariably pronounced and unmistakably perceived.'

mood or **tone** The prevailing state of mind or feeling of the poem which the writer appears to suggest to the reader and the overall emotional effect it generates. For example, one might speak of the sombre or lively tone or mood of the poem.

onomatopoeia A word whose sound imitates and therefore suggests its meaning as in bow-wow, hiss, whizz, crackle, cuckoo.

parody A piece of writing which imitates the characteristics of a writer's style with the intention of making fun of it. 'Terrible World' on p. 53 is a parody of the song 'Wonderful World'.

pastiche A piece of writing which imitates the characteristics of a writer's style.

personification Giving human shape or characteristics to something non-human e.g. an animal or an inanimate object or an abstract concept such as Peace, Love, War; or addressing an inanimate object or abstract quality as though it were a person as in

O Moon, look down from thy silver sphere

quatrain A four line stanza or group of lines which may have various rhyme schemes. The commonest verse form in English.

rhyme Identity of sound between words or verse lines in which the vowel and closing consonant sounds of a stressed syllable are repeated together with any weak syllables which may follow. In poetry, the letter or letters preceding the accented vowel must be *unlike* in sound e.g. *right* and *fight* which is a **perfect** or **complete rhyme** with two identically pro-nounced consonants (*t*) two identically pronounced vowels (*i*), a difference in the previous consonant (*r* and *f*), and two identical stress patterns. *Right* and *fight* are **one-syllable** or **single rhymes** but there are also **double** and **triple rhymes** as in the two or three syllable *making* and *baking* or *slenderly* and *tenderly*. One syllable rhymes are sometimes known as **masculine rhyme** and two syllable rhymes as **feminine rhyme**. Some rhymes may now appear incorrect simply because the pronunciation of words has changed over the years – *love/move*, *wind/mind* are common examples of what is sometimes known as **eye rhyme**. A writer may sometimes choose to soften the effect of rhyme by using **half rhyme** or **para rhyme** in which the consonant or the vowel is different. Wilfred Owen's poems 'Exposure' and 'Strange Meeting' make frequent use of this device, with half rhymes of words such as *brambles/rumbles*, *years/yours*, *spoiled/spilled*. Another common device is **internal rhyme** where a rhyme is used in the middle as well as at the end of a line as in

And pillows bright where tears may light

rhyme scheme The conventional way of noting the pattern of rhymed line endings in a stanza or a group of lines. The letter *a* is used for the first rhymed sounds, *b* for the second and so on. Thus we can say that the rhyme scheme of 'Ballad of the Bread Man' (p. 82) is *abcb*. The poem 'Funeral Blues' (p. 91) is arranged in couplets and its rhyme scheme is *aa*, *bb*, etc.

rhythm, stress, metre Rhythms and metres in English poetry are based on stress – the emphasis which we give certain syllables in *spoken* English. The pattern of groups of stressed and unstressed syllables in poetry together make up its rhythm. Thus when we say *Monday* the first syllable *Mon* is stressed and the second *day* is weak, whereas when we say *amuse* this pattern is reversed. The classic approach is to suggest that we can indicate patterns if we mark the weak and strong stresses in a line by using / to indicate a strong stress and x to indicate a weak one. In the line

  x / x / x / x /   x /
A book of verses underneath the bough

we can see that there are ten syllables to the line which fall into five pairs, each with an unstressed syllable followed by a stressed one. This unstressed/stressed pair is very common in English verse and is known as an **iambic foot**. Where, as here, there are five such iambic feet in a line, it is called an **iambic pentameter** (*penta-* simply meaning *five* as, for example, in *pentagon*). Other lines containing different numbers of feet (from one to eight) are monometer (1), dimeter (2), trimeter (3), tetrameter (4), hexameter (6), heptameter (7) and octameter (8).

After the iambic foot, the trochaic foot (stressed followed by unstressed: /x) is probably the most common in English verse

  / x / x / x / x
Home art gone and ta'en thy wages

There are several other patterns of syllables that according to classic tradition make up other different feet in English poetry such as the dactylic foot (stressed followed by two unstressed: /xx) and the spondaic foot (two stressed syllables: //) but we suggest that if you wish to pursue the matter further you should look to a specialist book such as *How Poetry Works* by Philip Davies Roberts (Penguin, 1986). You will find that in practice, stress patterns in English poetry are subtle and varied and that rhythms are rarely banged out in the mechanical manner that is perhaps suggested by applying classical rules of Latin scansion. It is more helpful for you to be able to hear and enjoy the dancing rhythm in this line

Love again, song again, nest again, young again

than to know that it could be said to consist of four dactylic feet.

run-on line(s)/enjambement Run-on lines of verse occur where the structure and meaning carry the reader's eye and ear directly over to the next line without a break. Enjambement reinforces this effect by ensuring that the second line has a weak rather than a strong opening syllable so that any break is even less noticeable.

simile (pronounced *simmily*: note the plural is **similes** pronounced *simmilies*) A comparison between two things introduced by the words *like* or *as*. (See also the notes on **metaphor** and **imagery** above.)

sonnet A poem of fourteen lines, each line being typically an iambic pentameter of ten syllables. The two main types are the **English** or **Shakespearean sonnet**, consisting of twelve lines made up of three quatrains (*abab, cdcd, efef*) plus a concluding couplet (*gg*) and the **Italian** or **Petrarchan sonnet** consisting of an octave and a concluding sestet. The octave is eight lines in two quatrains rhyming *abba, abba*: the sestet is composed of six lines rhyming *cdc, dcd*; or *cde, cde*; or *cd, cd, cd*. The **Miltonic** sonnet is based on the Petrarchan form but there is no pause between the octave and the sestet – which generally rhymes *cd, cd, cd*.

stanza Another word for a verse in poetry. A stanza has at least three lines, more often four and is usually rhymed in a pattern which is repeated throughout the poem.

stress All English speech has set rhythms of stressed and weak syllables. There is an agreed way of saying *Eng-lish* with an emphasis – or stress – on the first syllable *Eng-*; similarly the word *syllable* has a stress on its own first syllable.

syllable Words may be broken down into their constituent syllables – the small speech sounds that go to make them up. Thus *bro-ken* has two syllables; *down* has only one; *un-der-neath* has three … and so on. A syllable must include a central vowel and may be preceded by as many as three and followed by up to four consonant sounds. The way in which words are split into syllables in English is fairly arbitrary so don't worry too much about it: trust your ear rather than any mechanical principle. In a word with several syllables, one syllable receives the main stress though others may receive secondary stress and may be regarded as strong or weak according to what seems to suit the poem's metre.

syllabic verse Verse in which the total number of syllables in each line is regular. The poem 'Metaphors' on p. 37 has nine syllables to each and every line. In practice, the number of stresses per line, not the number of syllables is what most English readers notice. See also the note on pp. 211–212.

symbol Something regarded by most people as naturally typifying, representing or recalling something else because it has similar qualities or because it is generally associated with it. Thus white is a symbol of purity, the cross is a symbol of Christianity, the lion is a symbol of courage.

vowel An open and prolonged speech-sound made by using the mouth as a resonator as air is exhaled. A vowel can be a syllable on its own as *a* for example. The letters representing vowels are, a, e, i, o, u.

ACKNOWLEDGEMENTS

The editors and publishers wish to thank the following for permission to reproduce illustrations:

The National History Photographic Agency for the photograph on p. 6.

The Bridgeman Art Library for 'The Therapeutist' by Rene Magritte on p. 13.

AKG Photo for 'Die Lebensstufen' by Caspar David Friedrich on page 15, 'Death Wearing the Crown of the Holy Roman Empire' on p 45 and 'Les Constructeurs' by Fernand Leger on p. 116.

Magnum Photos Ltd for the photograph from the Washington Race Riots © Burt Glinn on p. 54.

The Imperial War Museum for the two signing up posters on p. 67.

King's College Library, Cambridge for the manuscript of 'The Soldier' by Rupert Brooke © Rupert Brooke Estate on p. 69.

The Hulton Getty Picture Collection Ltd for the photograph on p. 71.

The Press Association for the photograph on pp. 74–75.

The National Gallery for the Breugel on p. 81.

The Tate Gallery for 'Rocking Chair No 2' by Henri Moore on p. 97 and 'Elizabeth Siddall plaiting her hair' by Dante Gabriel Rossetti on p. 160.

Sally Greenhill for the photograph © Sally Greenhill on p. 98.

Bruce Coleman Ltd for the photograph © P Clement on p. 122.

Jo Osborn for the photograph of 'Alfie the cat' on p. 123.

Donald Cooper for the photograph on p. 140.

Corbis-Bettmann for the photograph on p. 141 and the photograph of Robert Frost on p. 171.

The British Museum for 'The Sick Rose' by William Blake on p. 149 and 'A Poison Tree' on p. 151.

The National Portrait Gallery for 'William Wordsworth' by Benjamin Robert Haydon on p. 152.

The Poetry Society for the photograph of Philip Larkin on p. 176 and the photograph of Liz Lochhead on p. 198.

Camera Press for the photograph of Seamus Heaney on p. 183.

Fotograf Dehlholm for the photograph © Forhistorisk Museum Moesgård on p. 189.

Carnet Press Ltd for the photograph of Gillian Clarke on p. 192.

The editors and publishers wish to thank the following for permission to reproduce copyright material:

Fleur Adcock: 'For Heidi With Blue Hair' reprinted from *The Incident Book* by Fleur Adcock (1986) by permission of Oxford University Press. Copyright © Fleur Adcock 1986.

John Agard: 'Anancy's Thoughts on Love' and 'Listen Mr Oxford Don' by permission of the author.

Maya Angelou: 'Phenomenal Woman' and 'Woman Work' from *And Still I Rise*, Virago Press Ltd.

Simon Armitage: 'I Am Very Bothered' from *Book of Matches*, Faber and Faber Ltd

W H Auden: 'Funeral Blues' from *Collected Shorter Poems 1927–57*, reprinted by permission of Faber and Faber Ltd.

Michael Benton: 'Sitting Sideways to the Sea' by permission of the author.

James Berry: 'Listn Big Brodda Dread Na!' from *Chain of Days*, Oxford University Press.

Edmund Blunden: 'The Pike' from *Poems of Many Years*, Collins Sons & Co. Ltd and reprinted by permission of A D Peters and Co.

B G Bollanack: 'Dunkirk', by permission of the poet and the Salamander Oasis Trust, previously published for *Schools' Oasis: Poems of the Second World War* (Editors: Dennis Butts and Victor Selwyn) and also *The Voice of War*, Penguin Books Ltd.

William Carlos Williams: 'The Red Wheelbarrow', from *Collected Poems*, Carcanet Press Limited.

Charles Causley: 'Ballad of the Bread Man' and 'Ten Types of Hospital Visitor' from *Collected Poems 1951–75*, Macmillan Publishers and David Higham Associated Ltd.

Gillian Clarke: 'Still Life', 'The Sundial', 'Overheard in County Sligo', 'No Hands', 'Miracle on St David's Day', 'Neighbours', 'Border' and 'Chip-Hog' from *Selected Poems, King of Britain Letting in Rumour*, Carcanet Press Ltd.

Merle Collins: 'No Dialects Please' from *Watchers and Seekers: Creative Writing by Black Women in Britain* edited by Rhonda Cobham and Merle Collins, first published (1987) by The Women's Press Ltd, 34 Great Sutton Street, London EC1V 0DX.

Tony Connor: 'A Child Half Asleep' from *Kon in Springtime*, reprinted with permission of Oxford University Press.

Wendy Cope: 'A Green Song' from *Making Cocoa for Kingsley Amis*, reprinted by permission of Faber & Faber Ltd.

Jeni Couzyn: 'Dawn', from *Life by Drowning – Selected Poems*, Bloodaxe Books.

e e cummings: 'next to of course god america I' from *Complete Poems 1936–62*, MacGibbon & Kee Ltd.

Keith Douglas: 'Behaviour of Fish in an Egyptian Tea Garden' from *Collected Poems*, Faber & Faber Ltd.

Steve Ellis: 'Gardeners' Question Time', reproduced with permission of the author.

Gavin Ewart (1916–95): 'Three Weeks to Argentina' with the permission of Margo Ewart.

U A Fanthorpe: 'You Will Be Hearing From Us Shortly', from *Standing To*, Peterloo Poets.

Vicki Feaver: 'Days', by permission of the author.

James Fenton: 'The Skip', from *The Memory of War and Children in Exile*, Penguin.

Robert Frost: 'Neither Out Far Nor In Deep', 'The Road Not Taken', 'Lodged', 'Nothing Gold Can Stay', 'Birches', 'Fire and Ice', 'Stopping By Woods on a Snowy Evening', 'Acquainted with the Night' and 'The Silken Tent' from *The Poetry of Robert Frost* edited by Edward Connery Latham, Jonathan Cape, reproduced with the permission of the Estate of Robert Frost.

Thom Gunn: 'Considering the Snail' from *My Sad Captains*, by Faber & Faber Ltd.

Seamus Heaney: 'Trout', 'Digging', 'Follower' and 'Death of a Naturalist' from *Death of a Naturalist*, 'From the Frontier of Writing' from *The Haw Lantern*, 'Bogland' from *Door into the Dark*, 'The Grauballe Man', 'The Tollund Man' and 'Tollund' from *North*, Faber & Faber.

Phoebe Hesketh: 'Days', 'The Leave Train', and 'I Have Not Seen God' by permission of the author.

Langston Hughes: 'Dream Variation', © 1942 by Alfred A Knopf Inc, reprinted from *Selected Poems of Langston Hughes*, by permission of the publisher.

Ted Hughes: 'The Thought Fox', 'Esther's Tomcat', 'Hawk Roosting', 'The Stag', 'Pike' and 'The Bull Moses', reprinted by permission of Faber & Faber Ltd.

Elizabeth Jennings: 'My Grandmother', from *Collected Poems*, Faber & Faber Ltd.

B S Johnstone: 'Song of the Wagondriver', from *Poems*, Constable and Co Ltd, by permission of the author.

Brian Jones: 'You Being Born' from *Spitfire on the Northern Line*, London Magazine Editions 'Stripping Walls', from *Poems*, London Magazine Editions.

Jenny Joseph: 'Warning' from *Selected Poems* published by Bloodaxe Books Ltd, copyright © Jenny Joseph 1992.

Rudyard Kipling: 'If', from *Rudyard Kipling's Verse: Definitive Edition*, Bantam Doubleday Dell.

Philip Larkin: 'Days', 'Next, Please', 'Toads', 'Toads Revisited', 'Love', 'Born Yesterday', 'The Whitsun Weddings', 'Ambulances', 'Going, Going', 'Afternoons' and 'Mother, Summer, I', reprinted by permission of Faber & Faber Ltd.

D H Lawrence: 'Baby Tortoise', 'Work' and 'Snake', from *The Complete Poems of D H Lawrence*, Heinemann Ltd, by permission of Laurence Pollinger Ltd and the estate of the late Mrs Frieda Lawrence.

Liz Lochhead: 'Riddle-Me-Ree', 'I Wouldn't Thank You For A Valentine', 'Revelation', 'Mo', 'The Choosing', 'Poem For My Sister', 'The Father', 'The Mother', 'Storyteller', 'Rapunzstiltskin' and 'Kidspoem/Bairnsang', from *Dreaming Frankenstein and Collected Poems*, Polygon.

Dennis MacHarrie: 'Luck', by permission of the poet and the Salamander Oasis Trust, previously published for *Schools' Oasis: Poems of the Second World War* (Editors: Dennis Butts and Victor Selwyn) and also *The Voice of War*, Penguin Books Ltd.

Norman McCaig: 'Movements' and 'Frogs', from *Movements*, Chatto & Windus Ltd.

Roger McGough: 'Defying Gravity' and 'The Hippopotamusman' from *Watchwords*, Jonathan Cape Ltd.

Edwin Morgan: 'Heron' and 'Glasgow Sonnet' from *The Second Life*, Edinburgh University Press.

Grace Nichols: 'Hey There Now!', 'Black', 'Be a Butterfly', 'The Fat Black Woman Goes Shopping' and 'Waterpot' reproduced with permission of Curtis Brown Ltd, London, on behalf of Grace Nichols. Copyright © Grace Nichols 1984.

Sylvia Plath: 'Metaphors' from *Colossus* and *Collected Poems – Sylvia Plath*, Faber & Faber Ltd, 'Morning Song' from *Ariel* and *Collected Poems – Sylvia Plath*, Faber & Faber Ltd.

Peter Porter: 'A Consumer's Report', Scorpion Press.

Margaret Postgate Cole: 'The Veteran', © H J D Cole, reproduced with permission of H J D Cole.

Colin Rowbotham: 'Relative Sadness', by permission of the author.

Siegfried Sassoon: 'The Rear Guard' and 'The Hero', from *Collected Poems*, Faber & Faber.

Carole Satyamurti: 'Striking Distance', from *Klaonica: Poems for Bosnia*, Bloodaxe Books.

Kenneth Slessor: 'Beach Burial', Collins, Angus and Robertson.

Raymond Souster: 'Flight of the Roller Coaster', from *Collected Poems of Raymond Souster*, by permission of Oberon Press.

Wole Soyinka: 'Telephone Conversation', from *Reflections*, African Universities Press.

Anne Stevenson: 'From The Motorway' and 'Poem for a Daughter', from *The Collected Poems of Anne Stevenson, 1955–1995* (1996) by permission of Oxford University Press.

Dylan Thomas: 'Poem in October' and 'The Hunchback in the Park', from *Collected Poems*, J M Dent & Sons Ltd, and by permission of the Trustees of the Copyrights of the late Dylan Thomas.

R S Thomas: 'Raptor' from *No Truce with the Furies* (1995), by permission of Bloodaxe Books.

Alice Walker: 'Poem at Thirty-Nine' from *Horses Make a Landscape Look More Beautiful* by Alice Walker, published in Great Britain (1985) by The Women's Press Ltd, 34 Great Sutton Street, London EC1V 0DX.

William Carlos Williams: 'The Red Wheelbarrow', from *Collected Poems*, Carcanet Press Ltd.

W B Yeats: 'He Wishes for the Cloths of Heaven' and 'The Wild Swans at Coole', from *The Collected Poems of W B Yeats*, Macmillan & Co Ltd.

Benjamin Zepheniah: 'Terrible World' and 'Neighbours' from *Propa* Propaganda, Bloodaxe Books; 'I Love Me Mudder (Mother)' from *The Dread Affair*, Arena, an imprint of Century Hutchinson.